Protein and
Nutrition Policy in
Low-Income Countries

Protein and Nutrition Policy in Low-Income Countries

FRANCIS AYLWARD
Department of Food Science,
University of Reading, England

and

MOGENS JUL
Danish Meat Products Laboratory,
Copenhagen, Denmark

CHARLES KNIGHT & COMPANY LIMITED
LONDON & TONBRIDGE

First published 1975 by
Charles Knight & Company Limited
25 New Street Square, London EC4A 3JA
& Sovereign Way, Tonbridge. Kent TN9 1RW

Distributed in Canada by
The General Publishing Company Limited, Toronto

© 1975 Francis Aylward and Mogens Jul

ISBN 0 85314–216–5
ISBN 0 85314–241–6 (paperback)

Printed in Great Britain

Foreword

by

Nevin Scrimshaw* MD

The world is entering a period when the relationship between food availability in low-income countries and rising population is increasingly perilous and, for some countries, has already reached crisis proportions. The technology symbolized by the term "Green Revolution" brought hope and sharply increased cereal yields to several of the most populous under-developed countries, but it has become clear that without an integrated nutrition and population policy it will not, in its present form, provide more than temporary relief.

The concentration on cereal production and improved cereal profitability to the neglect of legumes has resulted in a *per caput* decrease in their availability, even though legumes are an essential source of protein to complement the predominantly cereal diets of the majority of the populations in most low-income countries. Simultaneously, the price of legumes and of animal protein for these populations is rising not only because of decreased *per caput* production, but also because indigenous supplies are being drawn away by the rising demands of the affluent countries for more plant protein for animal feed and for meat and other animal products for direct consumption. A similar pressure reduces cereal supplies for low-income countries.

Little attention has been paid until recently to the fact that some affluent populations consume as much as 1800 lb of cereal per person per year because 80% of it is used for animal feed, while populations of developing countries subsisting largely on rice, wheat, or maize use less than 400 lb per person per year. Animal products are too costly to be a major source of protein for a considerable proportion of the world's populations. Moreover, world fish catches are reaching the

---

* Professor and Head of the Department of Nutrition and Food Science at the Massachusetts Institute of Technology, and Chairman (1970–73) of the Protein Advisory Group of the United Nations System

natural limits for many species, and some are decreasing. Recently, the rising cost of petroleum has increased the prices of fertiliser and the other agricultural inputs required to achieve the greater food production of the "Green Revolution". In addition, it is increasingly evident that the benefits of the "Green Revolution" tend to be spread unevenly, not only among the low-income countries, but also among socio-economic groups even in those countries where it has been most successful.

With this background of need for international as well as national action to avert the food crises that are at hand for most low-income countries, and that affect most seriously the cost and availability of protein supplies, this monograph is particularly timely. Many surveys of world food problems have appropriately emphasized the importance of the medical and social aspects of malnutrition. Others have dealt competently with the necessity for increased food production from agriculture and fisheries. Surveys focused on these topics are of great importance and are well reviewed by the present authors, but Drs Aylward and Jul have also given much needed and usually neglected emphasis to the post-harvest management of food supplies through improved storage, preservation, processing, and distribution. At the present time a significant proportion of the food supplies of low-income countries is lost to insects, rodents, moulds, and simple spoilage.

Unlike research and training designed to improve agricultural production, animal husbandry, and fisheries, there has been a notable paucity of research and training in the best means of preserving and processing food under the conditions prevailing in low-income countries, especially in the tropics. There are few research and development centres for food processing and food storage and there is a general lack of educational and training facilities for food and nutrition science within the university and technical school systems. This book makes a strong case for the establishment in such countries of more university centres for food and nutrition science and of centres for technical training in food storage and processing.

The book was commissioned by the Protein Advisory Group of the United Nations System to provide a general review of protein and energy problems in the world and of the efforts of the agencies of the United Nations System to deal with them. It has been written primarily for non-specialists who have responsibility for food and nutrition programmes. It is intended to be of use in both industrialized and low-income countries to industrialists, government officials, educators, scientists, and all others concerned in any way with food and nutrition policies. It also provides a guide to the approaches taken by the various international agencies to the major world food problems and to the policies and programmes designed to help low-income countries deal with them. The importance of doing so for the health and well-being of their populations as well as for their economic and social development is beyond question.

The authors have performed a singular service by incorporating into this volume their extensive knowledge and first-hand experience of the efforts of the United Nations System to apply scientific and technical knowledge to the production, conservation, and distribution of food in low-income countries. The Protein Advisory Group is grateful to them, and to the Pye Charitable Trust for its cooperation in the publication of this volume under conditions that will allow for a wide distribution in low-income countries.

Acknowledgements

This book is based on a report prepared for the Protein Advisory Group. The Group recommended that the report be published but lack of financial means prevented the Group itself from undertaking this. In the preparation of the book the authors have revised the earlier manuscript extensively, so that information has been up-dated to January 1974. This means that the authors alone and not the Protein Advisory Group, its Secretariat, nor any of the United Nations organizations are responsible for the final wording of the text.

Each of the authors has served on the staff of the Food and Agriculture Organisation of the UN, and as officers or consultants of other UN groups. Over the past fifteen years they have lived in, or travelled in, a number of low-income countries, so that they have been able to study food and nutritional problems in different areas and to benefit from discussions with ministers, civil servants, scientists, economists, educationists and industrialists concerned with local and regional problems. The authors have had access to a wide variety of publications and reports and wish to acknowledge the cooperation and assistance of many different UN agencies and groups.

In collecting and evaluating data for the present work, one of the authors (MJ) received professional assistance thanks to a research grant from Danida, the Danish International Development Agency. The second author (FA) wishes to acknowledge the assistance given to overseas activities in his department by the Nestle Foundation and the Leverhulme Trust, as well as support for travel from the (UK) Overseas Development Administration and the Inter-University Council.

Thanks are due to the publishers, Messrs. Charles Knight, for their interest in the volume, and to the Pye Charitable Trust for arrangements with the publishers, and for the generous grant which will enable copies to be distributed in official circles overseas. The royalties for the book will go to the Pye Foundation for the continuation of the Foundation's work for the promotion of food and nutrition studies.

Contents

Terminology

Different terms, such as *developing, less-developed, low-income, underprivileged,* have been used to describe the countries (mainly in Africa, Asia and South and Central America) which are the recipients of technical assistance. Many, but not all, are in the tropics or semi-tropics. Different countries are at different stages of development; sometimes attempts are made to divide into groups, *transitional* at one end and *very low-income* at the other. For convenience in this text, we have normally used the term *low-income countries* with the recognition that some of the countries concerned have potential or actual sources of wealth.

Names of some United Nations organizations

ACAST	United Nations Advisory Committee on the Application of Science and Technology to Development
ECOSOC	Economic and Social Council
FAO	Food and Agriculture Organisation of the United Nations
IAEA	International Atomic Energy Agency
IBRD	International Bank for Reconstruction and Development
PAG	Protein Advisory Group of the United Nations System
UNDP	United Nations Development Programme
Unesco	United Nations Educational, Scientific and Cultural Organisation
UNICEF	United Nations Children's Fund
UNIDO	United Nations Industrial Development Organisation
WFP	UN/FAO World Food Programme
WHO	World Health Organisation

Some abbreviations

FPC	Fish protein concentrate
LPC	Leaf protein concentrate
PCM	Protein-calorie malnutrition
SCP	Single cell protein

1. Introduction

1.1. International action

In 1963, the United Nations Economic and Social Council formed the Advisory Committee on the Application of Science and Technology to Development, ACAST. Its purpose was to report to the Economic and Social Council, and presumably, subsequently to the General Assembly on those areas where science or technology might best be mobilized to further development, particularly in low-income countries. In its deliberations, the Committee decided that one area where science and technology might contribute most was in respect to protein supplies and utilization. It submitted a report to this effect with a number of specific proposals for action. The report was adopted first by the United Nations Economic and Social Council in 1967 and subsequently by the United Nations General Assembly itself, and was published in 1968 under the title: *Feeding the expanding world population: International action to avert the impending protein crisis.* This aroused world interest to such an extent that it became one of the United Nations most widely sold and distributed publications, and it appeared that the world at large accepted that the subject was of the importance with which it was viewed by the United Nations system. In the years to follow, world protein problems became the subject of many national and international meetings, research programmes at universities and institutes and the concern of many well-informed individuals, as well as the public at large, in different countries.

The General Assembly of the United Nations, in a resolution in 1968, urged member governments to apply fully existing scientific and technological knowledge to improve protein supplies, distribution and consumption. The Assembly called for combined action—of national governments, of national and international scientific and educational organizations, of voluntary bodies and of the technical agencies of the United Nations towards this end.

1.2. The problem of malnutrition

The protein problem may be stated briefly; many individuals, families and communities in different parts of the world—and especially in

1

low-income, developing countries—do not receive a sufficient protein intake to meet their physiological needs. Protein malnutrition effects in particular *vulnerable* groups in a community, i.e. the pregnant and nursing mother, and the child at the breast, after weaning, and during subsequent early stages of growth and development.

Protein malnutrition is considered an important cause of the high death rates among children in low-income countries. Also, there is evidence (even if not conclusive proof) that protein shortages in infants and very young children can result in retardation in the development (perhaps irreversible) of the brain and nervous system. Although the full effects of deficiencies of protein and associated nutrients are still undefined, there are indications that the protein levels in the diet can affect adults as well as children and that low levels may reduce mental alertness and physical efficiency. There is increasing evidence that protein and other nutritional deficiencies result in greatly decreased resistance to infectious diseases, and conversely, that sick children have increased protein requirements.

It is now widely recognized that protein deficiency is only one aspect of a wider nutritional problem and that national policies should aim at adequate supplies of *energy foods* and adequate supplies of *all protective* and body-building foods. However, protein supplies warrant special attention for the reasons already outlined and because, in contrast to mineral or vitamin deficiencies, the physical amounts of protein required to avert malnutrition (when this exists) may require substantial changes in personal dietary patterns or (on a national basis) major adjustments in a country's food supply. Moreover, the widespread geographical occurrence of protein deficiency disorders provides a reason for international action.

The approach to the problem must be two-fold, namely efforts to improve food supplies generally, with parallel efforts to ensure that sufficient protein are available and, in fact consumed by the groups most in need.

1.3. Action by national governments

Following the 1967 discussions in the UN General Assembly it was decided that a questionnaire should be sent by the Secretary-General to all member governments to enquire what action was being taken in respect to improve food supplies in general and protein consumption in particular. An analysis of the replies was prepared in mimeographed form by the UN Secretariat in September 1968 under the

TABLE 1. INDICES OF WORLD AND REGIONAL FOOD PRODUCTION*

Food production	Total					Per caput				
	1968	1969	1970	1971	1972[1]	1968	1969	1970	1971	1972[1]
	(1961–65 average = 100)					*(1961–65 average = 100)*				
Western Europe	115	115	117	122	121	111	109	111	114	113
North America	115	115	113	124	121	108	107	104	113	109
Oceania	128	123	121	129	126	117	110	106	111	107
Other developed market economies[2]	124	123	122	123	128	116	114	112	111	113
Developed Market Economies	**116**	**116**	**116**	**123**	**122**	**111**	**109**	**108**	**113**	**111**
Latin America	114	120	124	126	126	99	102	102	100	97
Far East[3]	113	118	123	123	121	100	102	105	102	97
Near East[4]	119	122	125	126	136	104	104	103	101	106
Africa[5]	113	118	119	124	126	100	102	101	102	101
Developing Market Economies	**114**	**119**	**124**	**125**	**125**	**100**	**102**	**103**	**102**	**99**
Eastern Europe and USSR	126	123	130	132	132	119	116	121	122	121
China and other Asian centrally planned countries	112	116	122	125	124	103	104	107	108	105
World	**117**	**118**	**122**	**126**	**125**	**107**	**105**	**106**	**108**	**105**

* FAO: *The State of Food and Agriculture*, Rome 1973
1 Preliminary
2 Japan, Israel and South Africa
3 Excluding Japan, and China and other Asian centrally planned countries
4 Excluding Israel
5 Excluding South Africa

title—*The Protein Problem: Report of the Secretary General.* It showed that efforts were being made to increase food supplies in many low-income countries and that several industrialized countries were engaged in problems of overseas development in this field.

In examining the replies and the subsequent development it is evident, however, that there is no room for complacency. In one important respect progress has been made over the past years, namely the greater awareness of the problem in different countries. In a great number of countries good progress has been made in achieving increased food production, although in most low-income areas this has been counter-balanced in whole or part by population growth, cf. Table 1. It appears that improvements in overall food supply had taken place but—according to general belief—less progress in respect to protein supplies. The UN Advisory Committee on the Application of Science and Technology to Development suggested that development programmes should be regularly reviewed and when necessary recast to take protein problems into account and to consider such factors as:

(a) the necessity of speedy action.
(b) the means of mobilizing the scientific resources and industrial experience of industrial countries.
(c) the identification and removal of bottlenecks at different stages from primary production of protein to consumption of protein in food.
(d) the production and utilization of protein from non-conventional sources.
(e) the identification of specific projects for basic and applied research which will require financial support.
(f) the need for special attention to the protein requirements of the pre-school child.

1.4. The Protein Advisory Group of the UN system

Three United Nations agencies—the Food and Agriculture Organisation (FAO), the World Health Organisation (WHO), and the United Nations Childrens' Fund (UNICEF)—have been particularly active as regards protein and general nutritional problems since their foundation; for some years they have been advised as regards their activities in respect to proteins by the *Protein Advisory Group of the United Nations System* (PAG), of which they have been sponsors for several years.

The International Bank for Reconstruction and Development (IBRD or the "World Bank") and the United Nations' Secretariat have recently become co-sponsors of the Group, and other agencies of the United Nations, e.g. the United Nations Educational, Scientific and Cultural Organisation (Unesco), the United Nations Industrial Development Organisation (UNIDO), the International Atomic Energy Agency (IAEA) and the United Nations Development Programme (UNDP) take part in the meetings of the Group which in turn maintains contact with the United Nations' Advisory Committee on the Application of Science and Technology to Development (ACAST). The UN/FAO World Food Programme (WFP) is considering making a voluntary contribution to support the work of the Group.

1.5. Scope of the present publication

This book has been prepared in the hope that it will promote and encourage investigations and action in regard to food and nutrition problems. In Part II suggestions are made for various lines of action which may be recommended to low-income countries using their own resources or with the support of industrialized countries and of the United Nations system. As a background to any consideration of such action, a summary is given in Part I of the present state of nutritional knowledge of proteins, the nature and extent of protein deficiencies and the sources of food protein.

It is suggested that the time has come for special efforts within low-income countries to apply existing knowledge in this field. From high-income countries and from aid agencies renewed efforts are necessary in working out priorities for action in food and nutrition problems.

It is evident to the authors that uncertainty or even confusion exists in the field of protein nutrition in that the widespread existence of protein deficiency has been interpreted as a sign of insufficient world *production* of protein. The available evidence suggests that the production of protein is sufficient in practically all countries, even those in the very low-income group, and certainly more than ample in the world as a whole. The existence of protein deficiency is, therefore, in the main due to insufficient protein *consumption* of special groups. The reasons for this low consumption, often in the face of adequate supplies, are found in many factors, the most important probably being:

(i) Food patterns, which do not secure adequate protein intake,
(ii) Marginal incomes, resulting in edible proteins being sold, often exported, rather than consumed by those in need, and
(iii) Protein losses during harvest, storage, processing and/or cooking.

This being the case protein deficiencies can be counteracted by increased production only to the extent to which it makes edible proteins cheaper or more accessible preferably without a negative effect on the income of agricultural producers. However, it is clear that the factors mentioned under (i), (ii) and (iii) require interventions in many activities having little or no relation to actual production.

In many reviews of food resources, it has frequently been tacitly assumed that if food is produced it will also be eaten by those in need. This is far from the truth. Often, cereals are used for feeds rather than foods. Also, foods may be sold, often exported, by those most in need because they believe that they need the money more than the food. Thus, many protein deficient groups sell the proteinaceous foods they produce and keep, or buy, protein-deficient foods simply because the latter are cheaper, and satisfy the only nutritional need of which they are aware, i.e. their appetite. This points to the necessity of a greater diffusion of nutritional knowledge.

Food supplies depend not only on the existence of agricultural and fisheries production but equally on means of transporting, storage, processing and marketing. In our proposals we have stressed the importance of *post-harvest* problems embracing food storage, conservation and processing, namely the area stretching from farm to consumer which has received only fractional attention in many low-income countries in comparison with the very significant efforts put into agricultural production. While no one would suggest that efforts to increase production should be diminished, there is a need, in many parts of the world, for speedy and effective action in the post-harvest field, for example in the promotion of education and training in food and nutrition science, including food processing and marketing, and the encouragement of research and development work aimed at the growth of food, preservation and processing industries.

We would emphasize the importance of encouraging personal initiative and voluntary action inside low-income countries in relation to the food problem. It is often overlooked that in nearly all industrialized countries an important contribution to the food economy comes from *small-scale* production, through small holdings and kitchen gardens, *and* utilization, through village processing and small-scale processing enterprises owned by families and cooperatives. Such enterprises often depend in part on technologies, different from those now used in large scale food industries. In this connection there is need for detailed surveys and documentation on special techniques appropriate for use in low-income countries. An approach based on *appropriate technology* is recommended as complementary to other lines of action in which the total scientific and technological resources of the world are mobilized to deal speedily with nutrition problems.

PART I

PROTEINS, PROTEIN DEFICIENCIES AND THE SOURCES
OF FOOD PROTEIN

2. The Nutritional Background

2.1. Principles of nutrition

The needs of the human body for protein must be considered against the broad background of nutritional knowledge obtained by experimental work over the past hundred years and illumined by epidemiological studies and by the examination of the dietary habits of mankind. The general principles of human nutrition as given in standard text books may be summarized under a few headings.

Components of food. Most foods consist of a mixture of chemical compounds which may be classified as follows:

> Carbohydrates
> Fats
> Proteins
> Minerals
> Vitamins and other accessory factors
> Water
> Fibre

For the maintenance of life and bodily functions, man requires a mixture of the above food components, together with oxygen from the air.

Energy requirements. Of these components, carbohydrates and fats are the primary sources of the energy required by the body, for the maintenance of internal biochemical and physiological functions (such as digestion and absorption and metabolism of foods, the circulation of the blood, the activities of the nervous system) and for external activities. Proteins can also be used as a source of energy.

Requirements for nutrients. Proteins, minerals and vitamins are necessary for the building-up of body cells, tissue and organs, for the replacement of tissue wastage, the formation of many essential chemical components of the body (such as the enzymes required in digestion and the hormones required for control of various activities) and for various special functions—such as milk formation in the nursing mother.

Minerals are relatively simple inorganic substances; the vitamins and other accessory factors are more complex compounds containing carbon and other elements. At least ten vitamins and twenty or more (including trace) elements are essential, i.e., they cannot be manufactured in the body and must therefore be supplied in the food. Among the vitamins are one (or more) fatty substances ("essential fatty acids") which are constituents of some, but not all, natural fats.

Protein composition. Proteins are the most complex of all natural substances. From a chemical point of view they are made up of units known as amino-acids. Over twenty such units are known; the different food and body proteins contain varying numbers of these amino-acid units in different proportions and arranged in different ways. Different types of protein (for example those in meat or milk or cereals) owe their distinctive qualities to the four-fold variation in: the types of amino-acid units present; their relative quantities; the order in which they are linked together; and their structure in space.

Proteins can be broken down in the body—or in the laboratory—to the simple amino-acid units; the building up (or synthesis) of proteins from the smaller units can take place in the human body and in other living organisms. Within certain limits amino-acid units can be converted to one another, but there are at least eight amino-acids (the so-called *essential* or *indispensible* amino-acids) which cannot be synthesized in the human body, and which must therefore be supplied in the diet.

Protein mixtures. Food proteins differ considerably in their amino-acid composition. Animal proteins (for example from milk or meat) normally contain a mixture of amino-acids (including the essential amino-acids) the balance of which is rather similar to the proteins in the human body. In relation to this, plant proteins may be markedly deficient in one or more of the essential amino-acids; these essential units may be completely absent or present in only small amounts. Thus many *pure* plant proteins may have a lower "protein value", i.e. more protein has to be ingested to fulfil the requirements for all essential amino-acids. In a few cases, one essential amino-acid may be almost totally absent, so that the protein source, taken alone, would be insufficient regardless of the total intake of it. The essential amino-acid which is present in the relative lowest amount is referred to as the *limiting* amino-acid. It is for this reason that many plant proteins, when eaten as the only protein source, may be inadequate as sources of food protein.

However, in *mixtures* of proteins, deficiencies in one essential amino-acid in one component may be compensated by its presence in another component. Thus, even two proteins of poor nutritive value may *supplement* one another, e.g. a poor quality protein of plant origin may become of much higher value if mixed with a relatively small percentage of a second plant protein. This concept of *supplementation* has emerged from research work of the past twenty-five years and is of great practical importance.

Balanced diets. From the above it can be deduced that one should think not in terms of an *ideal diet,* but rather of *suitable diets*; it is possible to obtain the various components required for energy purposes (carbohydrates and fats) and the various nutrients (minerals, vitamins, essential amino-acids) required for protective and body building purposes, from a wide range of *mixed* foodstuffs. Good nutrition normally results from a balanced mixture of foods of different types; poor nutrition results from a diet restricted in quantity or quality, in particular (and most frequently) from diets which are limited to a few starch or fat-rich commodities.

2.2. Under-nutrition and malnutrition

Under-nutrition is the general term given to shortage of calories, which may or may not be accompanied by deficiencies in nutrients. Under-nutrition can arise from actual food shortages, from low food consumption arising from poverty, from loss of appetite, or from disorders of the digestive system or other metabolic problems which prevent the body from utilizing fully the nutrients in the food. In its extreme form, often referred to as *marasmus,* under-nutrition occurs in famines; it can lead to starvation and death.

During the present century much detailed information about under-nutrition has been gained from controlled experiments on volunteers undergoing complete or partial fasting or dietary restrictions for short or long periods; and also from studies in prisoner-of-war camps, among civilian populations of the different countries in Europe during and at the end of World War II, and of some of the more recent disaster areas. Thus, there is now a considerable body of knowledge on the biochemistry, physiology and pathology of moderate as well as extreme under-nutrition, but there are still many gaps in knowledge of conditions where deficiencies in *calories* occur in conjunction with deficiencies in *nutrients.*

The term *malnutrition* refers specifically to the effects of deficiencies in one or more nutrients or in the lack of balance between nutrients. The history of nutrition throughout this century has been closely linked with the examination of deficiency conditions induced by laboratory experimentation and the correlation of this information with clinical conditions observed by the physicians or recorded in medical or other literature.

The early work on vitamins led to the recognition of various deficiency diseases. Some of these such as scurvy (vitamin C, i.e. ascorbic acid deficiency) and rickets (in part vitamin D, i.e. calciferol deficiency) were at one time well known in Europe and North America; others such as beri-beri (deficiency in Vitamin B, i.e. thiamine) were formerly common in tropical and semi-tropical countries. Parallel investigations demonstrated the importance of several inorganic elements (or "minerals") in human nutrition. Thus, deficiencies in calcium and phosphorus were correlated with poor formation of bone and teeth; deficiencies in iron with problems of haemoglobin formation in the red-blood cell; deficiencies of certain other "minor" or "trace" elements with other pathological conditions.

2.3. Application of nutritional principles in high-income countries

What was described in the 1930s as the newer knowledge of nutrition has been applied successfully both to man and—to an even greater extent—to the feeding of domesticated animals, in most of the industrialized countries of Europe, North America and elsewhere.

In such countries animal husbandry and animal feeding practices have been revolutionized by the cooperative efforts of the farmer, the agricultural scientist and the manufacturers of animal feeding stuffs. The proper composition of rations for cattle, pigs, poultry and other animals can be calculated with a considerable degree of accuracy for both major components and for vitamins and minerals; computer techniques have enabled feedmills to determine the most economic and efficient mixtures to meet both the quantities and quality required at different stages of growth and for periods of special needs, such as milk or egg production. In fact, far more is known in the quantitative sense about the requirements of domestic animals than about those of man.

The application of nutritional knowledge to man has taken place in the main through the teaching of home economics, through the physician and dietician in the hospital and out-patient clinic, through dentists, and through many other channels; national or local public health authorities, dietetic advisers and catering officers of schools and residential institutions, the quartermaster or victualling officers of national defence services, and through a multitude of general educational programmes aimed at the public at large. In many of the temperate-zone industrialized countries several once-prevalent deficiency diseases such as scurvy and rickets, have been virtually irradicated over the past half-century. In such countries, older types of deficiency diseases may be almost unknown except where they are brought about in limited sections of the population by a combination of poverty and other factors—as with the problems of elderly people living alone on a food pattern limited in range and in quality, or simply by individual failure to heed the advice so frequently given.

The validity of nutritional principles as applied to large populations was demonstrated in several countries during World War II when many of the nations involved had to implement food and nutrition policies as a condition for national survival. The methods employed in the United Kingdom have been well documented and are of special importance because of the magnitude of the problems faced—the supply of food for some 50 million people on an island which had for a long period imported 50% or more of its food—and of the success achieved, namely the recognition that the health of the people was in many respects better at the end of the emergency than at the beginning. This success was recognized in 1947 by the Lasker Awards Committee of the American Medical Association which recommended "Awards for scientific and administrative achievements to the British Ministries of Food and Health and to the four great leaders in this historic enterprise, Lord Woolton, Sir Jack Drummond, Sir Wilson Jameson and Sir John Orr". The committee believed that this was "one of the greatest demonstrations of public health administration that the world has ever seen". It is accepted that the key to the programme lay in the "successful collaboration between food scientists and the statisticians engaged in drawing up programmes; the first application of nutritional principles to a piece of economic planning".

Much remains to be done in both basic and applied nutritional research, for example to discover what trace elements and other accessory factors, some possibly still unknown, are important in human nutrition and to define more exactly the daily amounts of nutrients required under different physiological, pathological and environmental conditions. Many questions still remain unanswered regarding the effects of different levels of protein and other components in the diet and the quantities of proteins in relation to lipids and other substances. Some of the main health problems of industrialized countries including obesity and coronary heart disease may arise in large part from *over-nutrition*—excessive food intake combined with inbalances between the quantities of the major and minor components of the diet.

In spite of these gaps in knowledge, the general principle of linking food and nutrition science with economic planning is accepted in different degrees in industrialized countries of varying political and social philosophies. It is accepted also as a central feature of the policy guiding the development programmes of FAO, WHO and UNICEF in assisting low-income countries.

2.4. Food and nutrition problems in low-income countries

The delays in applying nutritional principles to low-income countries are the result of many causes—historical, geographical, climatic and economic. Many food and nutritional problems are a reflection of social and economic conditions and are intimately linked with the stage of development in a given country and with the general infra-structure of systems and levels of communications, education, and scientific and technical attainment.

The growth of nutritional knowledge in the first half of the century took place in universities, clinics and research centres in industrialized countries which had the scientific facilities for detailed studies of the composition of the staples (such as cereals, meat and dairy produce) and of the minor foods commonly eaten, and for studies of food patterns and levels of consumption, and of the biochemical and physiological effects of foods in individuals and groups living largely under temperate-zone climatic conditions. It was inevitable, therefore, that the applications of these principles should take place in these same countries where food and nutritional scientists were able gradually to convince colleagues in other branches of science and in economics, and later civil servants and politicians, that the new knowledge was important in respect to public health and social and economic policies.

Much inspiration for nutritional work was received at an early date from the tropical world—e.g. centres were established in India and other parts of Asia in the 1920s, but advances were limited in most areas because of the absence of suitable laboratories and personnel and financial support for detailed studies.

Apart from the difficulty in securing and applying knowledge, there is another important reason for the delays in the acceptance of food and nutrition policies in low-income countries. In the majority of such countries, malnutrition was overshadowed up to very recently by the illnesses and mortality rates resulting from tropical and associated diseases. Such diseases are still endemic in many areas, but over the past twenty years public health authorities, with the aid of vaccinations and newer chemo-therapeutic agents and through other measures, have been able to reduce the incidence of microbial and parasitic infections and to bring about some measure of control. Thus, the food factor in health has become more obvious, and its social and economic importance—as well as its importance to individuals and their families—has become more widely recognized.

3. Protein Needs in Low-Income Countries

3.1. Proteins in relation to other nutrients

In low-income countries the population may be subject to overall food shortages and/or to specific nutritional deficiencies. Thus in any one locality or region those concerned with food, agricultural and nutritional policies must aim at securing for the population adequate amounts of energy-yielding foods and of body-building and protective foods including proteins, vitamins and minerals. Similarly the physician or public health officer must be concerned with the total nutritional picture and the detection of calorie shortages and of protein, vitamin, mineral and other deficiencies.

Although shortages of minerals and vitamins can and do occur, these deficiencies can normally be treated without too much difficulty, partly because there is sufficient scientific knowledge to diagnose the better-known deficiencies and partly because treatment usually involves relatively small quantities of materials, which can often be given as supplements to the diet or as a medicine, without the necessity of major changes in dietary patterns.

The reasons why protein deficiencies require special attention include:

(i) the evidence available now points to the fact that apart from calorie-shortages, protein deficiency diseases must be regarded as the major cause of malnutrition in most low-income countries;

(ii) the deficiencies present special difficulties because of inadequate methods of diagnosis;

(iii) protein deficiencies are often linked with other deficiencies so that accurate clinical diagnosis and epidemological studies may be difficult;

(iv) proteins are complex from the chemical point of view; there are wide variations in the composition of proteins from different sources and variations in biological value brought about by storage, processing and cooking procedures;

(v) proteins are required in considerable amounts each day; deficiencies cannot (except possibly as an emergency measure) be dealt with through the provision of medicines; a permanent solution may involve changes in food patterns or food habits or food preparation methods, or permanent food supplementation;

(vi) protein foods are normally among the most expensive foods; their immediate provision in any one country may entail imports which can be difficult on general financial grounds or because of balance of payments; their provision from indigenous sources may involve changes in the practices of agronomy or animal husbandry or fisheries which in turn may be hindered by economic considerations and by older dietary patterns;

(vii) the food and agricultural patterns, and even more so, the dietary patterns, in most countries—and especially in non-industrialized countries—are integral parts of the cultural pattern, and as such cannot easily be changed.

These different points will be discussed in detail in subsequent sections.

3.2. Protein-calorie malnutrition

The term *kwashiorkor* was used by Cicily Williams in 1933 to identify a disease diagnosed in Accra, Ghana, and described in the local language as the "sickness the older child gets when the next baby is born". She noted that symptoms similar to kwashiorkor had been described in the medical literature in East Asia, Mexico and East Africa. It was not until the years following World War II that the full significance of these observations became apparent. By the early 1950s the newer public health measures (including the more extensive use of chemotherapeutic agents and antibiotics) had begun to reduce illness and mortality arising from malaria and several other tropical disorders; the incidence of other types of diseases, and especially those arising from nutritional deficiencies, therefore, became more obvious.

The publication in 1952 of a survey by Brock and Autret under the sponsorship of FAO and WHO provided evidence of the widespread occurrence of conditions corresponding to kwashiorkor throughout the tropical world. Since that date an expanding medical and scientific literature has emerged embodying the results of clinical and laboratory investigations and epidemiological surveys in many different countries. The two UN agencies primarily concerned, WHO and

FAO, have kept the matter consistently under review, through their joint Expert Committee on Nutrition, through the Protein Advisory Group and through field programmes. A high proportion of the field activities of UNICEF has been concerned with protein supplies and distribution and with nutrition education aimed at reducing protein and other deficiencies.

Over the past fifteen years it has become clear that there are difficulties in distinguishing between clinical conditions resulting from shortages of calories and those resulting from protein deficiencies. Often both calorie and protein deficiencies are involved and the clinician prefers to use the term *protein-calorie malnutrition* (PCM) to cover a wide spectrum of clinical conditions which may be associated also in some cases with specific deficiencies in vitamins or minerals.

The clinical symptoms of protein-calorie malnutrition are described in standard text books and were reviewed in detail in the Report of the WHO/FAO Joint Expert Committee on Nutrition. Protein deficiency diseases can affect any group in a population, but are particularly common in infants (especially at the weaning and post-weaning stage), in older children during the period of active growth when daily protein as well as calorie requirements are high, in pregnant and nursing mothers and in individuals suffering from infections and parasitic diseases, or in the convalescent stage after illness. Among these, children and nursing mothers are regarded as *vulnerable* groups, i.e. those most exposed to protein deficiency diseases. These diseases can arise because of low levels of protein in the diet and/or because of poor quality of the protein; they can usually be treated successfully (if diagnosed at an early stage) by providing adequate amounts of protein in a suitable form, together with a general improvement in the diet.

3.3. Evidence of protein-calorie malnutrition

The evidence for protein-calorie malnutrition comes from several sources—

  (i) direct observations by clinicians and other professional workers on children, and on individuals in other age groups;

  (ii) anthropomorphic (weight, height and other body) measurements;

  (iii) biochemical estimations of amino-acid, protein or metabolic products which can serve as indicators of deficiencies;

  (iv) mortality and morbidity statistics among children—especially those in the age group of 1–4 years;

(v) comparisons between mortality rates in different countries over the past 100 years.

3.4. Clinical, anthropomorphic and biochemical criteria

The first of the above are by far the most important, more especially when they can be correlated (as has been the case in many investigations in different countries) with evidence of the effects of protein foods in preventing the disease in sections of a community and of the curative effects of protein foods among patients diagnosed as suffering from kwashiorkor or related conditions. The other lines of evidence are of importance in themselves, but even more important when correlated with (i) and with the protein levels in the food supplies of the local community.

Because of the difficulties in placing clinical observations on a quantitative basis special efforts have been made both by clinical and laboratory research workers in different countries and by the staff of WHO to develop anthropomorphic and biochemical indicators. These are of great potential importance in the diagnoses of the early stages of protein-calorie malnutrition. Improved methods of early diagnosis are required to enable treatment to be commenced in time so that death rates can be reduced; improved diagnostic methods should provide a better understanding of the biochemical mechanisms leading to the onset of the disease, and lead to more refined and effective methods of treatment and better correlation of clinical data with dietary studies.

3.5. Mortality rates among children

Mortality rates of children of different age groups can be examined in terms of both history and geography. Table 2 gives some data of child

TABLE 2. INFANT MORTALITY. DEATHS OF INFANTS UNDER 1 YEAR OF AGE FOR 1,000 LIVE BIRTHS IN YEAR

Year	England and Wales	France	Sweden	U.S.A.	India	Ceylon
1901/5	138	139	91	—	—	171
1921/5	—	—	—	74	206	—
1952	27	41	20	29	116	78
1966	19	—	13	23	—	(58)
1968	18	20	13	22	—	50

mortality in a few countries over the past century. In all the countries listed the death rate has declined almost certainly as a result of three factors operating in turn and reinforcing one another; improved general hygiene including water supplies; improved methods for the elimination of infectious diseases of childhood; improved supplies of calorie foods for both urban and rural populations.

It is difficult to distinguish between the impact of these different factors and of the improvements, characteristic of all high-income countries, in the standard of living and in medical and social services including maternity and child health programmes. Improvements in food supplies and availability of special foods have undoubtedly contributed to the reduction of deficiency diseases such as rickets and it is highly probable that improved availability of protein and other protective foods has had a distinct beneficial effect on child mortality rates.

Many paediatricians and public health workers believe that the impact of nutrition on child health is revealed by a comparison of

TABLE 3. INFANT MORTALITY RATE. MORTALITY RATE FOR THE AGE GROUP 1–4 YEARS AND "SOCIO-ECONOMIC DEVELOPMENT INDEX"

Countries	A Infant Mortality 0–1 year	B Mortality in Children 1–4 years old*	A/B	Socio-economic Development Index
USA (1964)	24.8	1.0	25:1	111
United Kingdom (1964)	20	0.8	25:1	104
Sweden (1963)	14.2	0.6	24:1	103
Australia (1964)	19.1	1.0	19:1	93
Argentina (1963)	60	3.7	16:1	73
Venezuela (1962)	30	6.0	5:1	62
Chile (1962)	114	7.2	16:1	61
Costa Rica (1964)	75	7.5	10:1	50
Panama (1964)	42.7	8	5:1	48
Columbia (1964)	84	13.7	6:1	46
Mexico (1964)	64	12.7	5:1	44
El Salvador (1962)	70	16.0	4:1	32
Ecuador (1968)	86	16	5:1	31
Guatemala (1962)	91	16.9	3:1	21

From Report of the Joint FAO/WHO Expert Committee on Nutrition (Geneva 1970): FAO/WHO (1971).

* Per 1,000 live births.

death rates in the 0–1 year age group in contrast with figures for the 1–4 year group. In Table 3 these figures are correlated with socio-economic development indices as calculated by the UN Research Institute for Social Development.

In the first group (0–1 year) the majority of infants are nourished for some period at least on breast milk; in low-income countries breast feeding by tradition often extends into the second year. The period 1–4 years corresponds to the transition from breast feeding to adult diets and there is abundant evidence from clinical observations of the disorders that result (in the absence of suitable weaning foods) when the child is no longer able to obtain breast milk in adequate quantity or quality, or when it is displaced by the arrival of another child. The ratio between these two mortality rates is used because the influence of other major factors, e.g. infectious diseases, is assumed to be the same for the two age groups. Figures such as those given in Table 3 provide indications (confirmed by clinical observations) of widespread serious deficiencies in many areas; the mortality figures represent only a fraction of the population suffering from less acute nutritional disorders.

3.6. Extent of protein-calorie malnutrition

In discussing malnutrition at a symposium some years ago Dr W. R. Aykroyd, former Director of the Nutrition Division of FAO, stated "The most important evidence comes from direct observation, i.e. from what physicians can see with their own eyes", observations which have resulted in "an impressive volume of information coming from many parts of the world, about the prevalence of malnutrition in children attending hospitals and out-patient departments in the tropics and sub-tropics."

Over the past twenty years, studies on protein-calorie malnutrition have been carried out in most low-income countries and many reports covering different regions of the world have been published in medical and scientific journals. WHO has accepted responsibility for the collection of information from different countries and regions and has endeavoured to secure accurate quantitative data from community nutrition disease surveys, from hospital statistics and from other sources. Some of the figures available are given in Tables 4A, B and C.

The survey methods are being extended and refined but the figures given illustrate the magnitude of nutritional problems on three continents.

The 1970 meeting of the WHO/FAO Joint Expert Committee on Nutrition in its consideration of many different aspects of protein-calorie malnutrition discussed the problems of diagnosis and accurate recording. The committee noted that in low-income countries the prevalence of severe protein-calorie malnutrition appeared to range from 0 to 7.6% in children below 5 years of age, while the prevalence of moderate forms may lie between 4% and 43%.

The Committee concluded—"It is clear from the above information that it is difficult to provide at the present time even a rough estimate of the total number of malnourished children in the world, although it is obvious to everyone concerned that malnutrition in its different forms is widely prevalent in most developing countries".

TABLE 4A. PREVALENCE OF SEVERE AND MODERATE PCM AMONG CHILDREN (COMMUNITY SURVEYS—WHO DATA[1]). AFRICA.

Year	Country	No. of children examined	Percentage of cases of Severe PCM*	Moderate PCM	Total PCM
1963	Algeria	2105	5.9	16.6	22.5
1965	Nigeria	432	3.2	—	—
1961	Nigeria	1268	1.7	5.6	7.3
1964/65	Senegal	164	—	—	13.4
1965	Uganda (Ankole)	286	4.9	27.2	32.1
1965	Zambia	359	—	—	17.0
1964	Algeria (Sahara)	1188	5.4	—	—
1968	Kenya	353	1.0	25.0	26.0
1965	Tanzania (Hombolo)	401	3.2	17.8	21.0
—	Uganda		5.0	25.0	30.0
—	Zambia	1104	1.7–4.4	—	—
1969	Malawi (South)	619	3.2	25.8	29.0
1968	Tanzania (Kisarawe)	630	7.6	19.3	26.9
1969	Tanzania (West)	393	1.5	10.5	12.0
1969	Tanzania	551	0.5	7.3	7.8

[1] From WHO Report No. 485; 1972.
* Including weights below 60% of the standard weight.

TABLE 4B. PREVALENCE OF SEVERE AND MODERATE PCM AMONG CHILDREN (COMMUNITY SURVEYS—WHO DATA). THE AMERICAS

Year	Country	No. of children examined	Percentage of cases of Severe PCM*	Moderate PCM	Total PCM
1966	Peru (Puno)	3313	0.5	4.4	4.9
1966	Chile	1540	2.6	32.0	34.6
1967	Costa Rica	738	1.4	9.0	10.4
1967	El Salvador	574	3.3	20.9	24.2
1967	Guatemala	763	4.1	24.5	28.6
1967	Honduras	633	2.0	20.5	22.5
1967	Nicaragua	708	1.4	11.1	12.5
1967	Panama	624	0.6	11.0	11.6
1968	Colombia	3378	1.7	19.3	21.0
1958/68	Mexico (Rural areas)	5576	3.4	27.5	30.9
1958/68	Mexico (Urban areas)		1.3	14.8	16.1
1967	Windward Islands (St. Vincent)	2490	1.5	25.7	27.2

* Including weights below 60% of the standard weight.

TABLE 4C. PREVALENCE OF SEVERE AND MODERATE PCM AMONG CHILDREN (COMMUNITY SURVEYS—WHO DATA). ASIA

Year	Country	No. of children examined	Percentage of cases of Severe PCM*	Moderate PCM	Total PCM
1962/64	Pakistan	1020	2.7	—	—
1963/65	Indonesia	1958	—	—	18.0
1969	India	15000	1.4–2.9	16.0	17.4–18.9

* Including weights below 60% of the standard weight.

3.7. Effect of protein-calorie malnutrition

The clinical symptoms arising from different forms of protein-calorie deficiencies are discussed in detail in the above mentioned FAO/WHO report. In the extreme form the deficiencies, unless treated in time, lead to death, but it is now recognized that moderate deficiencies may also be of great importance.

One area of current research deals with inter-relations of protein-calorie malnutrition and infections. Current knowledge has been reviewed in WHO publications as well as in reports in medical journals. There is now strong evidence that protein and other dietary deficiencies can accentuate the effects of infections, and that infections can accentuate the effects of nutritional deficiencies in both children and adults. Thus, it appears that periods of protein malnutrition will lead to greatly increased susceptibility to infectious disease. In addition, periods of disease—and the child in a tropical, low-income country is often sick 30% of the time—result in greatly increased requirements for protein. Moreover, infectious diseases generally result in loss of appetite and therefore, in reduced protein intake. To make matters worse, mothers frequently feed a sick child a liquid or semi-liquid diet, often a thin gruel or sugar water, i.e. unintentionally a low protein diet. Thus, the interaction of protein deficiency and disease may cause the most serious cases of protein-calorie-malnutrition. This view was amplified by the Protein Advisory Group in its Statement No. 20, issued in 1973.

It is clear from the above that protein deficiency problems in low-income countries would be greatly reduced if infectious and endemic disease could be prevented; however, this is beyond the present resources, but should be taken into account in the planning and implementation of programmes.

A second area of research is concerned with the possible effects of deficiencies in protein and other nutrients on the brain and other parts of the nervous system in the infant during the first months or years of life. Work on experimental animals has indicated that protein deficiencies can retard the development of the brain and lead to irreversible changes. The question is obviously of very great practical importance. Efforts are being made to extend investigations in this field so that adequate information may be obtained as speedily as possible. However, there is already much evidence to support the assumption that protein malnutrition in the foetal stage and first months of life results in retardation of brain development and that subsequent history of adequate nutrition cannot correct the defect. Protein malnutrition later in life, i.e. after the first months after birth, also results in decreased mental development and apathy, but does not seem to result in permanent damage; recovery may be complete provided that protein intake is adequate. However, this condition will seldom be fulfilled for the population groups affected. An exacerbating factor is found in that protein deficiency normally results in an apathetic, emotionless child. This may affect mother-child interaction and thus also indirectly impair child development. The Protein Advisory Group in its statement No. 18 issued in 1972, has commented on this.

3.8. Protein supplies, intakes and human needs

Where evidence of protein deficiencies are found we have to consider first if this is a result of inadequate supplies or (and this is probably more frequently the case) the result of unfortunate dietary patterns, e.g. protein foods are exported and starchy foods consumed, protein foods are eaten mainly by the men, or protein foods are simply too difficult for the small child to eat—as in the case of some meat and legumes—and, therefore, little consumed by this group.

Where protein-calorie malnutrition occurs the aim must be to improve protein intakes and to reduce requirements by preventing disease. The former mostly require a change in dietary patterns but may require also an improvement of supplies. Intakes must rise at least to the physiological minima but it is, of course, nutritionally desirable to provide amounts above the minima because of the indications (difficult to demonstrate in laboratory experiments) of some relationship between dietary protein and general well-being and physical and mental efficiency, and because of the greatly increased requirements of that part of the population which suffers from illness. The late J. C. Drummond, with his unique experience as Chief Scientific Advisor to the Minister of Food in the United Kingdom in World War II, speaking in 1948 about the problems of securing adequate food supplies stated his belief "that an immense range of literature" could be summarized by saying that "statistically there is a high correlation between efficiency in its widest sense and a rich protein diet—a low intake of animal protein is seldom coupled with high efficiency". As explained elsewhere, newer knowledge indicates that the necessity of *animal* protein can be disputed, but the advantages of good supplies of protein are accepted by most nutrition workers. Further investigations on the possible relation between protein levels and working efficiency are urgently required; they could be of special value in low-income countries where both industrialization and urbanization are taking place rapidly.

The area in low-income countries where action is most likely to be needed in respect to protein can be summarized in terms of two points:

(i) the necessity of making special provision for protein-rich foods for the needs of infants who cannot be breast-fed and during the weaning period;

(ii) the necessity of raising general protein intake in a country and improving effective distribution to ensure that all can obtain their physiological minimal required intake, and the desirability of increasing intakes still further to obtain (the still undefined) optimum amounts of protein.

3.9. Conclusions regarding protein nutrition in low-income countries

The attention given by the United Nations system and many other bodies to world protein nutrition has lead to some misunderstandings. Thus, it was often believed that total world supplies of edible proteins were insufficient to cover human needs. Table 7 in conjunction with Tables 4A, B and C confirm that supplies are ample, but so unevenly distributed within countries or even regions that deficiency is widespread. Others have postulated that the main problem is one of regional or seasonal under-supplies of caloric foods. It was felt that if only total food supplies are adequate, then most, if not all, diets are sufficient in their protein content to eliminate protein deficiency problems. In this assumption insufficient recognition is given to the high protein need of the sick child and of the pregnant and lactating mother.

Since considerable misunderstanding exists in this area, the Protein Advisory Group at its meeting in June 1972 reviewed the matter and issued its Statement No. 20, which is reproduced in Appendix I.

4. Protein Supplies and Protein Consumption

4.1. Protein content of animal and plant produce

Tables 5 and 6 give figures for the protein content on a fresh and dry weight basis of some animal and plant produce. Animal produce such as meat and fish, milk and eggs, is high in protein per kg dry weight, the main variations in meat and fish depending on the fat content, which in turn differs depending on the type of animal, its age and methods or habits of feeding.

The concentration of proteins in milk depends on several factors including the species of animal, the methods of feeding and environmental conditions. The protein level in cows' milk is higher than in human milk; cows' milk is, therefore, normally diluted when used in infant feeding.

Plant foodstuffs differ very considerably in their content of proteins; in general, legumes, oil seeds and cereals are relatively good sources; root crops, plantains and vegetables are poorer sources. Great variations are found within these groups; thus wheat is a good

TABLE 5. PROTEIN CONTENT OF ANIMAL FOODSTUFFS*

Source	Fresh Tissue		Protein g/100g dry wt.
	Water g/100g	Protein g/100g	
Meat			
Beef	70	20	67
Pork (lean)	70	20	67
Liver	70	20	67
Milk	87	3.4	26
Eggs (whole)	73	12	46
Fish			
Fatty (herring fillet)	63	17	46
Non-fatty (haddock fillet)	81	16	84

* The figures refer to uncooked produce. As wide variations occur in supplies from different animals, the figures quoted should be regarded as rough indications.

TABLE 6. PROTEIN CONTENT OF SELECTED PLANT PRODUCE*

Source	Fresh Tissue		Protein g/100g dry wt.
	Water g/100g	Protein g/100g	
Cereals			
Wheat	15	12	Î4
Maize	11	10	11
Oats	11	10	11
Rice	12	8	9
Oil-seeds			
Soya	10	33	37
Groundnuts	6	27	28
Cotton-seed	8.5	20	21
Sesame	5.5	21	22
Non-fatty legumes			
Peas	65–80	4.6–8.2	26
Beans	64–89	2.9–4.1	29
Green leafy vegetables			
Cabbage	90	1.4–3.3	24
Spinach	92	2.3–5.1	46
Roots, tubers and plantains			
Cassava (Manioc)	57	0.7	2
Potatoes	76	2.1	9
Yams	69	2.1	7
Plantains	60	1.0	3

* The literature shows very wide variations depending on cultivar, cultivation and other conditions and no doubt in some cases analytical methods.

source of protein; a second cereal—rice—much poorer. Within any one type of crop there are further variations depending on genetic strains, cultivation methods and environment. Thus Canadian (hard) wheat may contain 15% protein, English (soft) wheat less than 10%.

The range of variations in any one crop (or animal product) is not always appreciated; standard tables of analysis must be used with caution and ideally analyses should be carried out on the material under discussion. This is especially true in tropical countries, because far fewer analyses have been done on tropical—as distinct from European and North American—foodstuffs, and the range of variation may well be greater.

The actual protein content of the foods as actually eaten often differs from the figures for crop analysis. Thus, if wheat is milled to give white flour of say 70% extraction, much protein is removed with the germ and the bran. Milling or similar processing methods, although they may be designed primarily to reduce the amount of fibre or indigestible material, may alter the ratio between the different nutrients. Processing methods can sometimes be used to increase protein levels; thus, the modern air classification process can give a wheat flour fraction high in protein, with a second fraction low in protein.

One general point about nutrient levels is frequently overlooked; the actual nutritive value of a food depends not only on its *content* of nutrients after storage, processing and final preparation before consumption but also on the amount of the food regularly *consumed*. In spite of the importance of animal protein in high-income countries, plant proteins make a very considerable contribution to protein supplies there; thus, in the United Kingdom wheat flour contributes 30% of the daily protein; in some other countries the figure is even higher. In several European countries, e.g. Poland and Ireland, the potato has in the past made an important contribution to protein intake, in spite of its low protein content, because of the large quantities consumed.

It is generally recognized that legumes (e.g. ground nuts, beans, peas) contain quite substantial amounts of protein. Less attention is paid the protein content of what are considered *low protein* sources, especially cassava and plantains. Yet, because of the great quantities in which they are often eaten, their contribution to protein supply may be important. Their protein is deficient in some amino-acids but due to the supplemental effect (see 4.2 below) this will be rectified if even very small amounts of other foods containing protein are taken also. Therefore, they are clearly of importance in considering the food balance sheets of an adult population in low-income countries.

"Low protein sources" are of more limited use for infants and young children. Infant foods (substitutes of human milk) and weaning foods must contain a more concentrated source of protein because of limitations in the total bulk of food that can be eaten and often also because the difficulty encountered in digesting the somewhat coarser foods.

4.2. The relative value of animal and plant proteins

There has been much debate since the beginning of the century on the biological value of proteins from different sources. Many of the earlier experiments on *purified* individual plant proteins showed that these are often deficient in one or more of the essential amino-acids and therefore, when eaten alone, of poor value in relation to proteins from animal sources. The older views that animal proteins are of high biological value and plant proteins of low value were crystallized in the report of the Mixed Commission of the League of Nations in 1935 which stated categorically that some quantity of animal protein was essential. As mentioned above, more recent knowledge indicates that this statement, often quoted, is almost certainly incorrect.

Investigations over the past thirty years have shown that:

(i) whatever the deficiencies of *isolated* individual plant proteins, the *mixed* plants proteins as they occur in nature (e.g. the wheat grain or the potato) may be of relatively high value and

(ii) mixtures of plant proteins from different sources can be of good biological value because of supplementary effects—deficiencies in an essential amino-acid in one being counterbalanced by the amino-acids in another, and

(iii) the biological value of plant proteins may be increased by *fortification* namely by the addition to the protein of individual amino-acids, some of which, notably lysine and methionine, can now be produced on an industrial scale by chemical or biochemical syntheses.

Methods for the evaluation of protein quality are considered in detail in standard text books and have been the subject of reports by FAO/WHO joint committees (1965, 1973). The various methods were recently reviewed at a meeting in Reading, England. Although there is no doubt that animal proteins are of high value and that some plant proteins are of lower value, it is now generally accepted that diets consisting of mixtures of plant produce only can supply adequate quantities of protein.

This has been demonstrated under controlled investigations on *vegans*, i.e. complete vegetarians who unlike many vegetarians abstain from both eggs and dairy produce. It has been shown that some of the advantages ascribed to animal protein arise in part because of the presence in animal products of non-protein material such as minerals, vitamins and accessory factors, which may be absent from many plant materials. Thus the vegan may suffer from anaemia because of lack of vitamin B_{12} unless he takes steps to include a source of B_{12} in his diet (this is now standard practice among vegan groups in many countries).

This question of fortification is important in relation to the newer protein foods to be discussed later. If plant protein concentrates are to be used in infant foods they must be fortified (as recommended by the UN Agencies) with various nutrients; supplementation may also be desirable if plant protein concentrates are to be used widely by adults as single foods, rather than as components of mixed foods.

Some plants contain anti-metabolites (which may interfere with the utilization of protein and other nutrients) or toxic factors. Thus the soya bean contains a factor which interferes with trypsin, an enzyme in the human digestive system. Intake of raw soya bean may, therefore, interfere with digestion and cause pathological conditions. The substance, the so-called antitryptic factor, is removed by cooking and most types of processing or preparation. Similarly, cassava (manioc) may cause cyanide poisoning if not properly leached before cooking; cottonseed contains a toxic factor, gossypol, which must be removed before the seed can be used as food.

The utilization of plant protein in the body may be limited because of the structure of the foodstuffs; thus cell walls and other fibrous material may reduce the digestibility of the food and the assimilation of nutrients.

One obvious advantage of animal proteins in human nutrition lies in the fact that their amino-acid pattern closely resembles human tissue proteins, so that the body receives a "package" of amino-acids in approximately the correct proportions, whereas with plant proteins the mixture has to be "assembled". Mixed diets have been recommended by nutritionists throughout the present century; in low-income countries problems frequently arise from the restricted nature of the dietary patterns and from the high consumption of some one or two food staples which are low in protein and which in the normal dietary pattern cannot be adequately supplemented by other foods.

4.3. Protein resources

Information about the food resources can be obtained for a country from statistics of agricultural and fisheries production, imports and exports. The statistics when expressed in terms of actual foodstuffs can provide some measure of information about the total calories, proteins and other nutrients. Such calculations form the basis of the *Food Balance Sheets*, published at intervals by FAO, the latest in 1971 for the 1964–66 period. They are also used in tables showing net food supplies, contained in FAO's annual *Production Yearbook*, which gives net food supplies *per capita* for most countries in total calories, proteins and fats. Such figures are reviewed also in FAO's annual statement on the world food situation, the *State* of *Food and Agriculture*, and are the basis for FAO's studies of future needs for agricultural and food development, published in the *Indicative World Plan for Agricultural Development* and *FAO's Agricultural Commodities Projections* (1971).

It is recognized, of course, that there are many possible sources of errors in such calculations, firstly in securing accurate and reliable statistical data (for example in respect to home produced and minor foods), and, secondly, in converting the data to figures for nutrients as produced, and to nutrients as available for actual consumption, and actually consumed. Figures of wastage and food losses and analytical figures for the composition of food as actually consumed may be unavailable and have to be estimated. There is frequently a lack of information on proteins in the individual foods, on the biological value of the proteins, and on the value of the mixed proteins as actually eaten.

With these limitations, national figures for foods available can be expressed on a *per capita* basis (cf. Table 1), but further difficulties arise due to regional and seasonal variations and in relating supplies to consumption by individuals in different families and of different age groups, because of uneven distribution of supplies in different social and economic groups, in urban and rural communities, and within the family.

The broad pattern in terms of different regions of the world is given in Table 7—this shows that relatively low levels of both animal and total protein are characteristic of regions composed largely of low-income, non-industrialized countries.

The global data are presented in another way in Figure 1 which divides countries into seven categories in descending order of protein intake. This picture is in harmony with public health data on the distribution of protein-calorie malnutrition and reveals the special difficulties of countries (mainly in Africa) where the staples are roots, tubers and plantains and other countries (mainly in Asia) dependent on rice as the major staple.

4.4. Surveys of food consumption

A second method of obtaining estimates of food consumption is through surveys of actual food consumption of individuals, families and communities. Such surveys are valuable, but they are time-consuming and expensive, requiring cooperation on the part of the consumer and the use of well trained personnel for the planning and

TABLE 7. AVAILABLE SUPPLIES IN ENERGY, PROTEINS AND FATS PER CAPUT PER DAY BY REGIONS IN 1965[1,3]

Area	Energy Total calories	Proteins[2] Available supplies		Fats Total fats
		Total proteins	Animal proteins	
		(Grammes)		(Grammes)
WORLD	2374	65.5	20.7	55.0
ECONOMIC CLASS I	**2965**	**86.6**	**48.9**	**115.0**
North America	3166	94.0	66.4	146.1
Western Europe	2997	86.3	45.3	118.7
Oceania	3199	94.8	64.0	136.4
Other developed countries	2491	73.6	26.5	47.0
ECONOMIC CLASS II	**2120**	**54.7**	**11.0**	**35.1**
Africa	2154	58.2	9.3	37.4
Northwestern Africa	2051	57.9	9.1	38.2
Western Africa	2178	58.7	7.7	39.7
Central Africa	2086	43.7	10.1	36.7
East Africa	2186	63.1	11.0	34.8
Latin America	2470	63.7	23.7	57.8
Central America	2476	62.9	14.6	53.8
Caribbean	2326	56.5	21.8	53.6
South America	2488	64.9	27.0	59.8
Near East	2315	65.9	13.1	42.3
Near East in Africa	2305	66.9	14.2	42.8
Near East in Asia	2319	65.4	12.6	42.0
Asia and Far East	1984	49.4	7.6	27.0
South Asia	1965	50.5	6.8	27.3
East and southeast Asia	2025	46.9	9.5	26.2
ECONOMIC CLASS III	**2358**	**67.4**	**16.8**	**45.5**
U.S.S.R. and eastern Europe	3132	90.5	35.8	80.0
Asian centrally planned economies	2035	57.8	8.9	31.0

[1] Three-year average 1964/66.
[2] Provisional data expressed in local proteins.
[3] From Agricultural Commodity Projections, 1970–80. FAO, Rome, 1971.

execution of the enquiries and for the statistical examination of the results.

In general the results of the surveys published are consistent with the known distribution of protein-calorie malnutrition but the number of such surveys in low-income countries is still comparatively small; efforts are being made to extend and improve the consumption

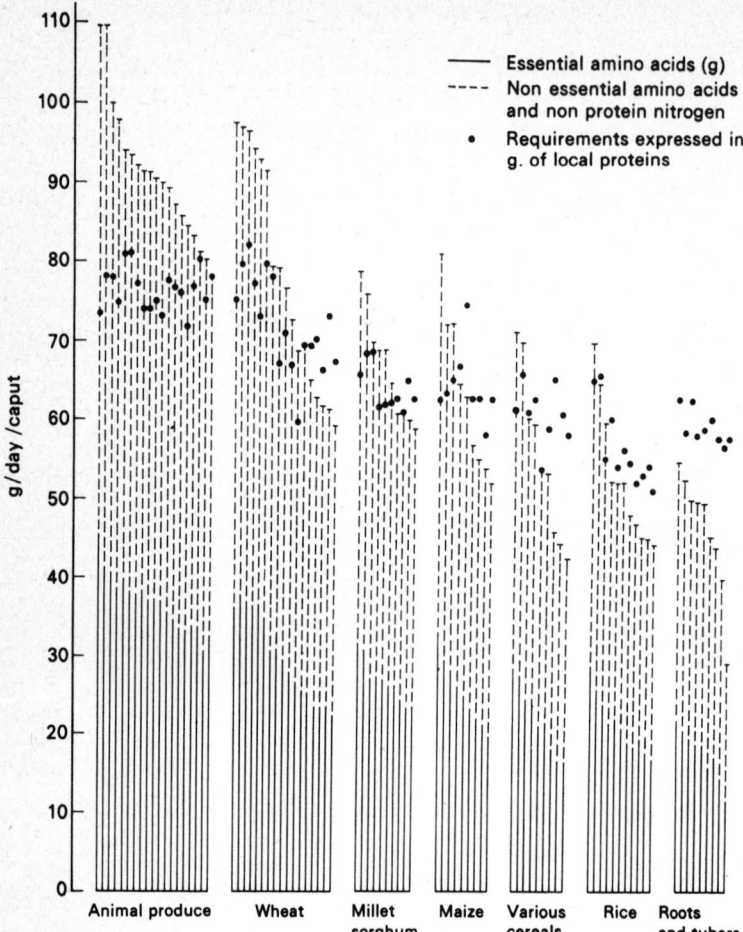

FIG. 1. ESSENTIAL AMINO-ACID CONTENT OF PROTEIN SUPPLIES
(From FAO, 1969. Provisional indicative world plan for agricultural development, FAO, Rome, 3 vol.)

List of countries arranged in descending order of total protein intake, and grouped according to type of main sources of protein.

Group 1, countries whose primary source of protein is *animal produce*: New Zealand, Uruguay, France, Argentina, Finland, Denmark, Ireland, Canada, the United States of America, Switzerland, Australia, the United Kingdom, Austria, Belgium–Luxembourg, Israel, Sweden, Norway, Federal Republic of Germany, the Netherlands.

Group 2, countries whose primary source of protein is *wheat*: Turkey, Rumania, Greece, Yugoslavia, Poland, Hungary, Italy, U.A.R., Spain, Chile, Afghanistan, Syria, Lebanon, Jordan, Iraq, Morocco, Iran.

Group 3, countries whose primary source of protein is *millet and sorghum*: Niger, Chad, Upper Volta, Sudan, Ethiopia, Senegal, Mali, Gambia, Nigeria, Tanzania.

surveys and to link them with data based on biochemical and clinical examination.

In actual practice, it has been demonstrated that even well organized teams experience considerable difficulties in obtaining accurate information on the food intake of the individual. In addition, the contents of nutrients in the food may not be known. Moreover, such surveys have to be extensive in coverage in regard to both time and area. On the whole, because of many inherent inaccuracies, such surveys have not been found as useful as could have been expected for diagnosing the nutritional status of an area. They can more appropriately be used in cases where nutritional deficiencies have already been found for determining the most appropriate course to follow in attempting to modify food patterns, and to alleviate the situation. For this purpose often less extensive surveys will suffice.

4.5. Correlation of *per capita* data and actual needs

Although *per capita* data on protein resources may give a useful background to nutritional surveys, it is now recognized that *per capita* data must be used with caution. In view of this the Protein Advisory Group issued in February 1971 a statement, PAG Statement No. 3, drawing attention to the many sources of possible error.

"The overall *per capita* availability of protein cannot be used as an indicator of the extent of protein-calorie malnutrition in a country because individual protein intakes may bear little relationship to physiological needs. If they can afford to do so, most persons will consume more protein than they require, often by a factor of two or three. Calorie intakes, on the other hand, bear a much closer relationship to actual requirements. It is noteworthy that according to FAO food balance sheet, Chile and Sweden have about the same *per capita* protein intake; yet protein-calorie malnutrition is a very serious problem in Chile and not at all in Sweden.

"It is well known that protein intake and quality vary greatly with socio-economic class. Whereas upper and middle-income groups

---

Group 4, countries whose primary source of protein is *maize*: South Africa, Mexico, Zambia, Malawi, El Salvador, Guatemala, Honduras, Dahomey.

Group 5, countries whose primary source of protein is *wheat, maize and rice*: Paraguay, Brazil, Peru, Venezuela, Costa Rica, Columbia, Bolivia, Surinam, Ecuador.

Group 6, countries whose primary source of protein is *rice*: Japan, South Korea, Formosa, India, Malaysia, Madagascar, Mauritius, Thailand, Pakistan, Ceylon, Philippines.

Group 7, countries on *roots, tubers and plantains*: Cameroon, Ivory Coast, Uganda, Togo, Ghana, C.A.R., Gabon, Congo (Brazzaville), D.R. of the Congo.

usually have a satisfactory protein intake, low-income groups, which form a large percentage of the population in a developing country, often have an intake which is very low. Protein malnutrition is frequent in urban and semi-urban low-income groups which rely completely on the market for their food supply, and also in rural areas among low-income groups growing most of their own food supply under marginal conditions or working as labourers. Even within socio-economic classes there are wide variations in protein intake among families.

"Even where family intakes of protein and calories appear adequate those members of the family with special needs, i.e. the pre-school child and the pregnant and nursing woman, frequently receive less than their proportional share for a variety of social and cultural reasons. Thus the problem of protein-calorie malnutrition is also one of maldistribution which cannot be estimated from food balance sheets or data on overall *per capita* availability of nutrients.

"There are other major limitations to conclusions regarding the relative adequacy of protein and calorie intakes of individuals in developing countries. This is because their physiological requirements for protein are increased by frequent episodes of infectious disease which cause both a decrease in intake and in increased metabolic loss of protein from the body. If this cannot be compensated for by higher than normal intakes of protein after recovery from the disease episode, progressive protein depletion occurs with each episode. In young children this is a primary factor in the occurrence of the serious clinical form of protein deficiency relative to calories known as kwashiorkor. In addition, parasitic infections and diseases causing diarrhoea decrease intestinal absorption of dietary protein as well as other essential nutrients.

"The combined effect of these factors is to increase the *per capita* need for protein in developing countries particularly among pre-school children who suffer from frequent bouts of diarrhoea and other infectious diseases and harbour intestinal parasites of different kinds. Thus the FAO/WHO recommended allowances for protein based on the needs of individuals free of disease cannot be applied indiscriminately to the populations of developing countries. It has been suggested that the recommended allowances for pre-school children in developing countries may need to be increased substantially over those for advanced countries until improvements in environmental sanitation, personal hygiene and preventive medicine reduce the burden of infectious disease. While changes of this nature and magnitude will require many years much damage to health of the pre-school child may be prevented immediately by more adequate diets.

"Dietary intakes compared with recommended dietary allowances for pre-school children in developing countries may sometimes suggest calories to be more limiting than protein. Nevertheless, for the reasons cited, protein may still be the most critical deficiency in the diet and clinical signs of protein deficiency occur in some children. Moreover, the prevention and treatment of all forms of protein-calorie malnutrition in children usually require more concentrated sources of protein in relation both to calories and to total bulk than provided by existing diets.

"Conclusions as to the relative significance of combined protein and calorie deficits for all age groups are also confounded by the fact that individuals can adjust to calorie deficit by reducing their activity while their protein requirements are likely to be increased under the same circumstances because of the factors described above. In addition, it is important to recognize that any significant degree of calorie deficiency can exacerbate deficiency of protein because the protein in the diet is then used in part for energy purposes. This is a significant factor in the occurrence of the various forms of protein-calorie malnutrition in children.

"It is for all of these reasons that the nature and magnitude of the problem of protein relative to calories cannot be predicted from overall food availability data. It has been suggested in the FAO Indicative World Plan that even when protein supplies are 20% above the average national requirement, a significant part of the population may still have diets deficient in protein. The average *per capita* protein supply needed to avoid protein malnutrition will obviously vary considerably with the circumstances. It will tend to increase for the developing countries as incomes and effective demand rise.

"Prices of protein-rich food are likely to rise considerably in many countries, especially for animal products. Such foods will, therefore, be even more outside the reach of the underprivileged groups in the years to come, unless national food and nutrition policies are established to provide for vulnerable groups."

This statement has been quoted in full because it includes many points well known to nutritionists working in low income countries, but often ignored in the interpretation of data.

5. Protein Sources—Agricultural and other Systems

5.1. Classification

In Table 8 the primary sources of food are summarized under three main headings, firstly the traditional agricultural and fisheries systems, secondly other biological systems, and thirdly chemical and biochemical syntheses.

As Table 8 suggests, protein foods must be considered not only in terms of *sources*, but also of *products*. The common distinction between "conventional" and "non-conventional" is useful in classifying sources but unsatisfactory in relation to products. A more realistic classification may be made on the basis of:

A1. Foods from plant and animal sources obtained through normal agricultural or fisheries systems and consumed either in the raw or cooked state or following some well-recognized system of curing, preservation or processing.

A2. Foods obtained by extraction or similar forms of treatment of agricultural or fisheries products.

B. Materials obtained by microbiological syntheses or products derived therefrom.

C. Materials obtained by chemical or biochemical syntheses.

For ease of reference A1 may be described as *conventional*, A2 as *semi-conventional* and B as *novel or non-conventional*, and C as *synthetic*. There is over-lapping between the different categories; some foods are conventional in one region but unknown or unusual elsewhere. A protein-rich product such as yeast, which is in group B, has long been used as a food component. The new protein products from oilseeds, often considered non-conventional, are clearly in category A2.

It seems probable that over the next decade the major supplies of foods will continue to come from traditional sources, i.e. A1, but that important contributions can come from A2. Nevertheless because of the projected growth of population and for economic reasons plans must be made to make use of categories B and C, with the recognition that the main *initial* contribution to human protein supplies from

40

TABLE 8. PROTEIN SOURCES

Primary Sources	Classification of Foods and Recent Developments	Examples
A. Agriculture or Fisheries *Plants—Land* Agronomy—field crops Horticultural crops Home gardens & allotments Wild produce	A1 *"Conventional"** Modification or extension of conventional sources.	1. Success in introducing soya in the U.S. in 1930's. 2. New high yielding varieties of wheat or rice. 3. High protein varieties of maize.
Plants—Sea or Water Produce of inland waters & water culture Produce of seas *Animals—Land* Animal production Small animal production Wild life	A2 *"Semi-conventional"* New foods based on products of agriculture or fisheries.	1. Edible protein from soya, cotton, rape, groundnut and other oil seeds 2. Edible protein from chlorophyll-containing material ("leaf protein") 3. Protein concentrate from fish ("FPC").
Animals—Seas and Inland Waters Fish and other animal produce		
B. Other Biological Systems —Uni-cellular or more complex organisms	B1 *"Non-conventional" or "Novel"*† Production from non-agricultural (or fisheries) systems	Proteins obtained by the action of uni-cellular organisms on carbohydrates or petroleum. (i.e. types of "SCP").
C. Chemical or Biochemical Systems	C1 *"Synthetic"*‡ Synthetic materials are usually components rather than complete foods.	Commercial production of amino-acids.

* A food may be conventional in one area (e.g. soya in Asia) and novel or unknown elsewhere.
† Food yeast may be regarded as prototype of protein material produced by uni-cellular organisms.
‡ The production of *ammonia*, an essential component of fertilisers and also of biological protein-producing systems (B), is a major activity of the chemical industry. Urea, also produced by chemical syntheses, is used as a component of ruminant feed.

micro-organisms will probably be *indirect* through utilization as animal feed. This indirect contribution can be of value in various ways, firstly by achieving economies in other sources of foods, previously used as animal feed, secondly through liberating land for other purposes, and thirdly in making available more animal protein for human use.

5.2. Crop production

There is now a body of scientific and technical information and experiences on the methods available for the improvement of agronomic practices and crop yields; the marked rise in agricultural productivity in industrialized countries over the past half-century has demonstrated how scientific principles can be applied with success to crop production.

In many low-income countries national governments, frequently assisted by bi-lateral development agencies, by international foundations and by FAO, have taken steps to expand agronomy and to raise production. Significant improvements have taken place in many countries over the past decade.

The general expansion of agronomy—in terms of field and horticultural crops—should in any one country lead to a greater supply of energy-yielding foods, but unless appropriate priorities are agreed, there may in this be little direct relief to the protein deficiencies which may be prevalent in areas where root crops, plantains and rice are the staples.

The FAO agronomy programme, which to a large extent forms the basis of the advice given to agricultural authorities in low-economic countries, advocates intensive efforts to increase total crop yields, with a stress on crops supplying significant amounts of protein. Legumes are clearly of great importance, but cereals must also be included in protein programmes. As already noted cereals in several European countries contribute 30% or more of national protein supplies; in low-income countries cereals normally have an even more important role. It is advocated therefore that special efforts be made to improve the yields and protein content of local crops, especially cereals and legumes.

Investigations of the Ford and Rockefeller Foundations in conjunction with research groups in different countries have demonstrated the potential contribution of the new high-yielding varieties of cereals, more especially if these have not only high disease resistance, but also increased protein content. High protein cereals represent one of the simplest approaches to the improvement of supplies of dietary protein, in that the additional protein is potentially available for use without the necessity of changes in food habits.

If this last point is to be achieved, investigations must take into account the *end-use* of the cereal—so as to ensure that the varieties recommended are not only high in nutrients, but have the technical characteristics for use in actual food preparation. If this ideal cannot be reached, it is important to "define" the changes (e.g. in milling practices, recipes and baking or cookery procedures) to enable the cereals to be used. When foods are produced for processing, quality must be defined both in *nutritional* terms and in terms of *function*. Intensive research and development efforts are still required for the breeding of protein-rich high-yielding varieties of crops suitable for different geographical areas and for different types of end-uses. The Protein Advisory Group in its Statement No. 8, issued 1970, called attention to these and similar problems.

Public attention has recently been focused on the achievements of programmes for high-yielding crops but there is a growing realization that while these developments have been very spectacular, many problems are far from solved.

In the first place, agricultural outputs depend in large measures on agricultural inputs; increased protein production from agronomy must be linked with high fertiliser inputs; as the production of ammonia and other fertiliser components may depend on the establishment of a chemical industry, success may come primarily to countries or regions in which some growth of heavy industry has already taken place. Moreover the new seeds may be of most use to the well-established large scale farmer, as distinct from the small-holder. The higher yields achieved by the farmer may force prices down, thereby placing the latter in a precarious situation so that he even may have to cease producing.

Further comments have been made by scientific workers who refer to ecological and historical aspects. Agronomy has traditionally depended on the use of a very large number of varieties of any one crop; famines resulting from crop failure through drought or disease have been most obvious from mono-cultures. It can be argued, therefore, that only when a large number of new varieties are in use can there be a sense of security with a reasonable hope that new problems will not arise through plant diseases.

For the above and other reasons most agricultural advisers believe in the diversification of approach in low-income countries with attention to different types of plant produce—including those from home-gardens and allotments—and with full use of, and improvements of, indigenous plants. In all such programmes the avoidance of waste—of loss of crops in the field, at harvesting and during post-harvest storage and processing—is an important additional objective.

5.3. Land animal production

Animal production represents a direct way of increasing supplies of high quality food protein. The experience of high-income countries has been mobilized in many low-income countries to promote animal production through the eradication of disease and through better breeding, feeding and management practices. FAO and other reports describe the continued and intensive efforts in many low income countries to achieve increases in animal protein supplies.

The difficulties in many low income areas are formidable—because of endemic diseases, shortage of water and feeding stuffs, unfavourable environmental conditions and lack of local experience. Many authorities believe that the greatest possible use should be made of indigenous animals which may be the more resistant to disease, and better adapted to the ecological conditions. It will normally be unwise for a tropical country to follow in all respects established patterns of temperate-zone regions. Protein can be produced by any species of animal and a choice should be made with full knowledge of local circumstances and local ecological patterns.

Many programmes for increased milk production are based on the dairy cow using the patterns from the industrialized countries, but FAO has stimulated programmes for the use of animals other than the cow; the sheep, the goat and the water buffalo already make an important contribution in many areas.

In respect to meats a number of countries especially in East Africa are using indigenous animals and are exploring actively the possibilities of improved game farming. Attention is being given to the use of small animals as well as cattle; thus several countries have been able to introduce rapidly large scale poultry and egg production and in other areas rabbit production is being encouraged.

From the point of view of protein supplies, milk and eggs are of special importance because they may most easily be used as supplementary foods to improve the quality of an otherwise limited and mostly vegetarian diet for small children.

5.4. Fisheries

Few aspects of protein production have received greater emphasis than fish supplies both from the sea and inland waters. Surveys conducted in the early years of FAO noted the very wide differences in the availability and use of sea fish in different regions of the world. Thus in the Northern hemisphere, and especially in Northern Europe, Japan, North America and the Soviet Union, the fishing industry was well developed; commercial fisheries in other regions were often very limited and carried out with quite primitive methods. Many changes have occurred (often under the inspiration of FAO or bi-lateral programmes) ranging from the provision of outboard motors for canoes (as in West Africa) and other indigenous craft, to the establishment of modern fishing fleets with appropriate shore storage, processing and marketing facilities. This led to impressive developments, i.e. a world marine catch of more than 60 million metric tons as compared to 20 million metric tons prior to World War II.

Further growth is likely to be more difficult because present operations have already resulted in overfishing and decreasing yields in many of the best known, highly productive areas. New developments must concentrate mainly on two possibilities. The first is increased capture of species which at present are little utilized. However, for these a market will have to be developed and efforts of this kind have in the past proved to be difficult except where a fish meal industry can be developed. The second possibility is in the development of heretofore unused or little used resources, either on the high seas or by finding new fishing grounds or methods. All will require a costly development in capture vessels, gear, and new fishing methods; in most cases, markets must also be developed for these potential catches.

Thus, while the total possible yield from the oceans of conventional fisheries is estimated at some 150 million metric tons, achieving this will require much capital investment, innovation and training, and the resulting contribution to world protein supplies will not be cheap.

Reliance has sometimes been put in inland fisheries and FAO has been very active in this field. However, the total sustained yield from existing inland waters is not great. Attention has, therefore, been turned to fish farming. Where no feeding is applied, the yield per unit of area is approximately the same as the yield of meat animals from grassland; where the artificially reared fish is fed, the feed conversion rate is about the same as that of meat animals or in milk production based on artificial feeds. Thus, fish farming may be a useful alternative to agriculture, but yields are no greater than in farming.

On the whole, fisheries is an important part of the world protein supply system, yielding about 10% of total protein supplies, but a quick massive increase is improbable. It is more likely that by a sustained or even intensified effort to develop world fisheries, these will be able to maintain their present share of the world protein supplies. This in itself would be an important achievement.

Some concern has been expressed because recent development of refrigerated distribution systems have permitted the wider distribution of fish, the improved demand resulting in increased prices, thus making fish less accessible to low-income populations in coastal areas.

A considerable tonnage of fish is used as *fish meal* for animal feed, instead of for direct human consumption. The reasons are complex and include (i) fish is landed in an unsanitary condition, not suited for human food. Overcoming this would require improved preservation aboard which is very expensive, (ii) in other cases the catch takes place over such short periods that its preservation as human food becomes uneconomic, (iii) much fish meal is manufactured from fish scrap and offal, which would otherwise be discarded.

Efforts have been devoted to developing fish protein concentrates (FPC) for human consumption from resources such as edible grade fish or offal. However, it appears that the resulting product will be more expensive than originally anticipated, and will be difficult to incorporate in conventional diets. The Protein Advisory Group (1971) has commented on this subject in its Statement No. 16.

5.5 Proteins from other biological systems

Yeast is a good source of protein as well as other nutrients and efforts have been made at intervals over the past 30 years to develop special food yeasts to be used as food supplements. Although yeast preparations have been used in "health foods" in many countries, yet the use of whole yeast has had limited success; it can be employed only in relatively small amounts both because of its taste and its effects on the functional properties of the foods to which it is added.

The more recent investigations have been concerned with the growth of suitable micro-organisms (bacteria, yeasts and moulds) for more complex organisms such as algae, on a suitable carbon source with the use of ammonia or the equivalent as a source of nitrogen, followed by the purification of the protein formed to give the so called *single-cell protein* or SCP. The rationale behind such programmes lies in:

(i) the possibility of producing protein free from the hazards, uncertainties and environmental factors associated with agronomy, animal production or fisheries,

(ii) the potential advantages of controlled production under factory conditions,

(iii) the high efficiency of the micro-biological conversion of carbon sources with inorganic nitrogen to protein,

(iv) the speed of production in contrast to agriculture,

(v) the relatively wide range of uni-cellular organisms and of carbon sources, of which many hitherto could not be used for food production.

Many universities, research centres and industrial laboratories are now involved in intensive research and development work using different carbon sources—including some from agricultural sources (e.g. molasses, or low protein flour residues obtained as by-products from air-classification milling procedures), from the cellulose industry, from sewage and from petroleum and natural gas.

Microorganisms are not pure proteins. They contain many other components including small amounts of nucleic acids. These substances should not be present in human diets in unlimited quantities, because nucleic acid purines are excreted as uric acid, which in susceptible individuals may increase the possibility of gout or kidney stones. The nucleic acid content in SCP can be lowered by several methods.

The safety testing of SCP is clearly a matter of great importance when petroleum or similar compounds are used as substrates or when other organisms than traditional yeasts and algae are used, e.g. bacteria. Stringent tests must be undertaken to ensure the elimination of potentially harmful components, e.g. hydrocarbons.

Pilot plant production of single-cell protein now takes place in several centres in Europe, Japan, North America and the Soviet Union and extensive biological tests are now being carried out; in a few countries large scale production has been started. While a large part of the published work on microbial, algal and other proteins from non-agricultural sources deals with their use in animal feed, a number of research and development centres are concerned also with the use of the new preparations in human diets.

Microbial proteins are being used *initially* for the feeding of domestic animals rather than for direct human use. Such use as animal feed requires somewhat less stringent preliminary toxicological testing, in that up to a point the animal can act as a "filter" for materials unsuitable for direct use by man. Adequate testing of the flesh and other products (such as milk or eggs) of the animals are, of course, necessary and have been carried out with convincing results. Because of the economic importance of the animal feed industry there is strong industrial support for work on single-cell protein. Its use in animal feed may lead to important economies in making more cereals and oilseeds available for use in human food. In its Statement No. 4, the Protein Advisory Group (1970) outlines some of the problems in the use of SCP and the tests required before it can be used as human food.

5.6. Nutrients from chemical and biochemical syntheses

Several vitamins can be made in the laboratory and some are synthesized commercially. Some essential amino-acids, notably lysine and methionine, are made on a commercial scale. The price is moderate and will almost certainly decrease as production rises.

Animal experimentation has confirmed that synthetic amino-acids can be used to increase the biological value of proteins which are deficient in them. Thus the value of cereal protein can be increased by lysine and that of soya protein by methionine. Supplementation of this type is used in animal feeds and this procedure can make some contribution to total effective protein supplies.

Proposals have been made for the supplementation of human food with synthetic amino-acids (e.g. by the fortification of wheat by lysine). Many nutritionists prefer at this stage to advocate supplementation of proteins by other proteins (e.g. wheat flour by milk powder or soya flour) rather than by amino-acids. Questions of fortification (including amino-acid fortification) are reviewed in the Report of the 1970 Joint FAO/WHO Expert Committee for Nutrition. In practice fortification may be unnecessary for the bulk of the population in high-income countries, where protein dietary levels are relatively high and where supplementation does in fact take place through mixed diets (e.g. bread and cheese).

Even where one staple (e.g. rice, wheat or maize) in low-income countries forms a very large part of the diet, small amounts of other protein food (e.g. fish sauces, beans) are frequently used and may be sufficient to balance the amino-acid pattern of the total diet and make supplementation with any one amino-acid unnecessary.

If the *total* diet is deficient in one particular essential amino-acid and food fortification is to be considered, a proper vehicle has to be selected. It has to be one that is processed industrially and is distributed in such a manner that it reaches those groups of the population where the deficiency is found. In practice, amino-acid fortification may be difficult in low-income countries because of the absence of centralized milling and/or baking industries and also on economic grounds.

In choosing a vehicle for fortification other items apart from the main staples can be considered. Any food or drink or even medication may be used provided it reaches the group in need.

The Protein Advisory Group (1970) in its Recommendation No. 9 outlines steps for the amino-acid fortification programmes. There may be circumstances in which the procedure can be justified but further evidence is awaited from trials now in progress.

Some further products of chemical syntheses may be noted. Ammonia, produced from the nitrogen of the air, is, of course, a major component of fertilisers; it is essential in most uni-cellular systems of protein production and is used also (in combination with molasses and other components) in some feed formulations for ruminants. Other industrial products, namely urea, or often better biuret, can be used in ruminant feed; they can replace some proportion of the protein required by ruminants, as distinct from monogastric animals. Thus, their use in ruminant feed can lead to better use of the available naturally-produced feed protein, and of the land used to produce this protein.

There is scope for further experimental work to determine the optimum levels and other conditions of use of protein substitutes for different types of ruminants under varying environmental conditions. There is need also for investigations on the use of other synthetic substances which can be used as sources of energy in cattle and other domesticated animals. The question of animal feed composition, and the efficiency of protein production by both ruminants and monogastric animals is important in any consideration of ways and means of increasing protein supplies for human use. Problems of this nature are being investigated at a great many universities and agricultural research institutions.

6. Protein Foods

6.1. Food preservation and processing

Agricultural and fisheries products to be used as foods can be broadly divided into two categories; *perishable* and *less-perishable*. In this second category are cereals and root crops which under appropriate conditions can be stored for relatively long periods (e.g. from one harvest to the next); in the perishable category are most fruits and vegetables and all animal, including fisheries, produce.

Agricultural produce can be considered also in terms of commodities (such as fruits and vegetables, and also milk) which can be eaten raw, and other commodities which normally are eaten after some simple cooking or curing procedure, and a third group, such as cereals and oil-seeds, which are (often prior to cooking) subjected to milling or to some other form of processing.

In practice a large number of foods have to be stored or preserved or processed. *Preservation* is achieved through methods such as dehydration, canning or bottling, and freezing, or through the use of smoking, salt, sugar, acids and other chemical preservatives, with or without the use of protective packaging materials or special storage conditions. *Processing* includes such operations as milling (cereals, oil-seeds, sugar), baking, fermentation or cheese making. Preservation and processing techniques can form the basis of domestic, cottage or village operations, as well as of large scale food industries.

These techniques make a contribution to nutrition in several ways. Firstly, without the existing storage and preservation methods there would be much increased food losses through pests and microbial attacks. In spite of the methods presently in use such attacks constitute a loss of some 20–40% of the world's food supply. Therefore, this subject termed the "War on Waste" is the basis for one *area of concentration* in FAO's programme of work. The Protein Advisory Group (1969) has issued its Statement No. 7 on this subject.

Secondly, storage and preservation play a very important role in securing food supplies from one season to the next; without it, seasonal malnutrition would be rampant in many areas, even survival might sometimes be at stake. Thirdly, preservation and processing often form the basis for food distribution from one area to another and from continent to continent.

Fourthly, processing is often required to enable agricultural materials to be more easily digested and utilized in the human body. Lastly, preservation and processing extends the range of foods available and can add to the variety in the diet.

TABLE 9. PROTEIN FOODS—PURPOSE AND EFFECTS OF PROCESSING

Objective	Notes or examples	Applications to low-income countries
1. Avoidance of waste; storage, transport, preservation	Applied to all protein foods including animal products and cereals	Of special importance in tropical and semi-tropical countries because of adverse environmental condition (heat, humidity, insects and other pests)
2. To achieve extraction of (a) food components (b) feed components (c) by-products	Important especially for cereals and oil seeds	Older traditional methods (e.g. for cereals) may be unsuitable or ineffective in supplying needs of larger populations in an urban environment or reduce the protein content unnecessarily
3. To remove toxic or other unwanted materials	Essential for the utilization of many legumes	Important to allow greater utilization of indigenous materials
4. To achieve acceptability and utilization of food components	Protein isolates may be used direct as foods but more usually as components of the prepared foods	Changes in food patterns are normally slow in a traditional society and special methods are required to assure acceptance of new types of foods

In high-income countries preservation and processing industries have grown up parallel to agriculture, first as ancillary trades on or near the farm, and later as self-contained activities largely divorced from agriculture. The evolution of the food industries over the past 150 years has come about through scientific and technical developments in such matters as sources of energy and power, and types of equipment, processing methods and packaging materials. It has also been hastened in high-income countries by the needs of expanding populations living in large towns and by changes in patterns of working conditions, social life and of food habits. The pace of change in many countries has accelerated in the past two decades.

The food industries today require a background of scientific and technical support including trained personnel, of a calibre and with responsibilities (in respect to the scale of operations, range of products, and their importance in human nutrition) very different from, say, fifty years ago.

6.2. Importance in relation to proteins

Preservation and processing methods are of special importance for all protein foods and especially for animal products, cereals and oil-seeds. The different techniques which may be defined in terms of general principles must be adapted for the individual commodities, e.g. drying methods and conditions must be worked out for different types of fish, heat treatment and extraction conditions for different oil-seeds, milling techniques for different cereals.

In the past much of the development work on preservation and processing methods has taken place in industrialized countries with an emphasis on foods of special importance to such countries. Experimental work on post-harvest problems with special emphasis on indigenous crops is now urgently required *within* low-income countries. In the past the post-harvest problems have received much less attention in national and international aid programmes than agricultural production. In low-income countries work on *preservation* has often been limited to the storage of grain and other staples, and has been divorced from the wider developments in modern food science and technology, or it has consisted mainly of efforts aimed at introducing methods in use in industrialized countries into other parts of the world where they may not always be quite appropriate or useful.

There are historical reasons for this situation. In many high-income countries it has long been accepted that state assistance should be available to promote *agricultural* research and development and to maintain the agricultural sector of the economy. On the other hand commercial operations "outside the farm gate" (i.e. preservation, transport and marketing of foodstuffs) have often been divorced from the agricultural sector and—being in the province of private industrial initiative—received little or no aid from government agencies.

Over the past three decades this situation has been somewhat modified in many industrialized countries, and increasing support has been given from public funds to subjects related to food storage and processing, but low-income countries, in their internal administrative arrangements and other respects, have often followed the older pre-World War II pattern.

This tendency for development work intended to improve nutrition to concentrate primarily on agricultural production was reflected also in the organization and financing of the earlier stages of the United Nations involvement in rendering technical assistance. Thus, the Secretariat of FAO, the Food and Agriculture Organisation of the United Nations, was originally made up of large sections of agronomy and animal husbandry specialists, a few entomologists to consider problems of pest control during the post-harvest storage of agricultural crops but with only one food scientist or technologist, actually placed in the Fisheries Department (then Fisheries Division). While the governing body of FAO made possible a fairly rapid build-up of the agricultural services of the organization, a long period elapsed before specialists in food storage, preservation, processing and marketing were employed.

It may be symptomatic that they were first recruited in the Nutrition Division, probably because it was the nutritionist who, from field observations, realized that nutrition may not be improved by increasing agricultural production *alone*. The produce must be protected against losses, preserved to be suited for distribution or for storage from one harvest season to the next, and properly processed and cooked to be eaten and be of nutritionally good quality. Even today, the composition of the staff of FAO shows that this aspect of the organization's work is not receiving an attention commensurate with that accorded to other aspects of the programme, nor with the importance of these disciplines in improving the world food supply.

The situation has, however, received additional attention in recent years in FAO where more and more persons, competent in food science and technology, are being added to the staff. Another step was taken in 1972 when the Nutrition Division of FAO was transformed into a Food Policy and Nutrition Division, to work closely with FAO's Policy Analysis Division, in order that food and nutritional viewpoints might be constantly brought forward in planning FAO's programme of work.

The position in low-income countries will be discussed in greater detail later (Chapter 9). At this stage it may be noted that the gaps extend from education and training through research and development to support the often embryonic food industries. These gaps are of particular importance to protein supplies, for, as noted earlier, many protein foods are perishable and, therefore, in special need of preservation.

6.3. Protein concentrates from agricultural products

Protein concentrates such as dried milk or dried meat have long been known although greatly improved as a result of technological advances over the past fifty years. Cheese can be considered as a protein concentrate from milk; stock fish, a protein concentrate from fish; other examples can be quoted. In dietary practices mixtures of proteins are often eaten, the most obvious examples being bread and cheese, or vegetable soups containing cheese, meat or fish. Protein materials have been used also as components of manufactured foods such as soup mixes and of the many proprietary infants' foods which have been available in high-income countries since the end of the last century.

Concentrates from plant foodstuffs and especially oil-seeds have become available parallel to the growth of the vegetable oil-seed extraction and refining industries in Europe, the Soviet Union and North America and have been widely used throughout this century in animal feeding stuffs. Grass and leaf crop drying techniques developed since the 1930s have as their objective the provision of good quality protein and associated vitamin components for animal feed. Fish meal has also been widely used in animal feed.

Recent developments in the use of protein concentrates in human food follow investigations (see Table 10) that have taken place mainly over the past twenty-five years. These investigations, in the laboratory, pilot plant and industrial scale, have centred around (i) oil-seeds of different types and (ii) fish. More limited work in a laboratory and small pilot plant has been carried out on non-fatty legumes such as field beans and on chlorophyll-containing materials, e.g. leaf forage crops (to give what is known as leaf protein concentrate, LPC).

The impetus for research and development work on protein concentrates for human use has come from three directions: from commercial and governmental bodies in industrialized countries which aim at the more effective utilization of oil-seeds and other produce; from industrial organizations concerned with vegetarian and health foods; and from bodies interested primarily in the food,

TABLE 10. PROTEIN CONCENTRATES

Stage	Use
A. Production of protein concentrates *Animal sources* Dried milk Cheese Fish Protein Concentrate (FPC) *Crop sources* Oil seeds such as soya, groundnut, sesame, sunflower, cotton, rape Non-fatty legumes such as field beans Chlorophyll-containing material such as alfalfa (lucerne)	As component of other foods such as: bread milk substitutes weaning foods for children dietetic foods
B. Production of protein isolates (from A)	As components of other foods
C. Production of textured, spun or chewy gel products by extrusion or other techniques (as extension of B).	To produce meat and other analogues with form as well as texture to be used as substitutes or extenders

nutrition and health problems of low-income countries. These three streams of development have in no way been exclusive, in fact they have reinforced one another in different ways.

The industrial approach has arisen in part from a desire to make the maximum use of produce and by-products of agricultural raw materials. Thus in the United States soya and cottonseed are important sectors of the agricultural economy; the primary product in the past has been edible oils; the residues were used mainly for animal feed. There are clearly economic advantages in transforming the residues into human food, particularly because it is possible to obtain from the residues good quality protein at a lower price than from animal sources. Thus developments have been linked with consumer needs, with the rising costs of animal protein foods such as meat and dairy products and also with the *functional* use of protein concentrates in various manufactured foods, e.g. as water-binding or emulsifying components. Thus soya protein has been used for many years in breadmaking in North America and in some European countries, and lately quite widely in comminuted meat products.

The impetus arising from vegetarian beliefs and practices cannot be ignored. One of the major changes in dietary practices in this century has come from the introduction of processed cereal breakfast foods. Their introduction sprang in large measure from industrial and family enterprises imbued with a vegetarian philosophy. Their successors, represented now by a number of important food firms, may no longer be motivated by a vegetarian belief, but are active in development work on foods based in whole or part on plant protein concentrates, simply because these have proved to be inexpensive and nourishing foods.

The impetus for work on protein concentrates for use in low-income countries has come in large measure from FAO, WHO, UNICEF and UNIDO, and from different bi-lateral technical assistance agencies. Thus, FAO has assisted in setting up processing facilities and UNICEF has cooperated with manufacturers of concentrates for use in children's foods. The USA *Food for Peace* programme under the US Department of Agriculture has, in collaboration with the US Agency for International Development, developed some such foods for emergency feeding, notably "CSM", a mixture of maize, soya flour and dried skimmed milk, fortified with vitamins and minerals, which has been used extensively in emergency feeding situations. It is being manufactured by several large food firms.

Collection of information and review of these activities in respect to low-income countries has for many years been a responsibility of the Protein Advisory Group which keeps in close touch with developments in this field and reviews progress at its meetings and in its bulletin. The list of the Protein Advisory Group's publications (see bibliography) includes many related to protein concentrates.

6.4. Protein concentrate from oil-seeds

Protein concentrates can be obtained from different agricultural sources and from products of non-agricultural systems. The most significant advances have come so far from oil-seeds.

The potential advantages of oil-seeds as raw materials are (i) that they can be grown economically in many different regions of the world (different oil-seeds suit different environmental conditions); (ii) oil-seeds have a high protein content; (iii) as legumes they are efficient convertors of soil nutrients to protein; (iv) the other major component, namely triglyceride oil, has a place in the food economy in its own right; (v) other by-products may also be of value. The yields of protein and the amino-acid composition varies from one type of oil-seed to another; in general the proteins are of reasonably good biological value although they may be deficient in some one essential amino-acid and therefore of most value when supplemented or when used as supplements.

The main disadvantages of oil-seed proteins lie in the frequent occurrence of anti-metabolites (e.g. trypsin-inhibitors in soya bean). Such substances can often be destroyed by the correct choice of processing conditions, e.g. in soya beans by heat, but special problems arise with some crops, for example some cotton-seed cultivars have a high content of gossypol which must be removed if the seed extracts are to be used in human foods. Current research programmes in cotton-seed therefore include the breeding of cultivars low in gossypol while other efforts are aimed at mechanical means of separating the gossypol-containing glands from the flour.

Oil-seeds are extracted on a commercial scale in most industrialized countries. European countries use large quantities of seeds imported from tropical regions in addition to domestic crops such as sunflowers and rape-seed which can be grown in temperate climates. The United States has available domestically produced soya and cotton-seed; in Canada rape-seed is an important crop and much effort is made to develop it further, including finding varieties with a high protein content.

The oil-seed industry is based on the production of edible oil (used in the production of margarine and other fats) by either expressing (milling) or solvent-extraction methods. In the older pattern of industry, conditions were chosen primarily to give good quality oil without special regard to the quality of the protein residues. Some reduction in the biological value of the protein resulted mainly from the heat treatment. In the newer processing methods conditions are adjusted to protect the protein and steps are introduced for the removal of fibre to render the residue more suitable for food use.

More recent work (see Table 10) has involved not only improvements in preliminary extraction methods but the development of pure protein products such as soya protein isolates and also the use of extrusion spinning and other techniques to give *textured* materials, which can be used as components of manufactured foods. Much experimentation has gone into the development of flavours for such products, a technique which combined with texturizing processes results in quite satisfactory analogue foods, e.g. resembling meat, fish or cheese.

A recent study by Hammonds and Call, sponsored by the US Bureau of Fisheries, provides a full account of the very considerable impact of the protein products in the US market, in particular an impact on the dairy industry and on animal production generally. The last five years have witnessed very rapid developments in the production, distribution and sales of these materials in the United States where a variety of meat analogues and dairy substitutes are readily available.

The development of such analogues has been so successful that today 30% of the meat protein in school-lunch programmes in the USA may be replaced by such proteins in the form of meat analogues. This development is by no means limited to North America. Over the past years a similar pattern of change has been seen in the United Kingdom and in some other European countries and a large number of leading food firms in Europe and North America are now concerned in some way with protein concentrates.

In respect to milk there appears to be no agreed international nomenclature but a broad distinction can be made between:

(i) *Toned milks* in which the protein level is maintained by mixtures entirely of milk origin, e.g. buffalo milk (high in fat) with dried skimmed milk.

(ii) *Vegetable toned milks* as (i) but with the use of plant protein as an additive to the milk from the cow or other animal.

(iii) *Filled milks* in which the milk fat is replaced by, or supplemented with, vegetable oils.

(iv) *Substitute milks* in which the milk protein is replaced or supplemented by other vegetable protein, and the fat is replaced by vegetable oils. (Some substitute milks are derived entirely from plant materials.)

In India, where there is little prospect of supplying adequate amounts of milk for child feeding, widespread use is made of milk toning whereby available milk supplies are stretched and high quality protein is being distributed in an easily acceptable manner. One such programme is the so-called "Milk-Tone" project.

The introduction of protein concentrates in industrialized countries has undoubtedly been hastened by economic considerations, with financial advantages to the farmer and manufacturers as well as potential advantages to the consumer.

6.5. Protein concentrates from other sources

Although the main commercial successes in protein concentrates have been in relation to oil-seeds, research and development work has taken place in many other materials.

There has been a very considerable investment in fish based on the fact referred to above that there are large quantities of fish in different areas which could be preserved for use as food through the isolation of a stable protein rich meal or flour. Such products could be made from fisheries material which it is not normally possible to use direct as human food. The technical problems of edible fish flour, FPC, production have been largely solved through major technical research efforts.

Technical specification for these products, if they are to be used for human foods, have been developed by the Protein Advisory Group in its Guideline No. 9.

Several problems remain, however. First, unless expensive processing methods involving flesh separators and sophisticated extraction methods are used, the proteins are obtained by sedimentation, along with the finely ground bones. Thus, the product may be slightly gritty. Second, the sedimented products have low water-binding capacities and are, therefore, difficult to incorporate into most foods. Third, as mentioned above, landing fish in a human grade form is considerably more expensive than landing it for fish meal; therefore, the cost of FPC has proved to be considerably above that originally assumed and above comparable vegetable protein isolates. Statement No. 16 of the Protein Advisory Group outlines some of the main considerations which have to be made in considering the manufacture of FPC for the use in the diets of low-income countries. Some of the problems encountered in attempts to incorporate FPC and other protein concentrates into the diets of low-income groups are discussed below.

Protein preparations or concentrates can also be obtained from other animal produce either from animal foods (such as meat or milk) or from produce normally discarded or used for non-food purposes (e.g. blood and other human grade abbattoir material, whey from cheese manufacture). Dried skimmed milk, now readily produced as good quality and stable material is, of course, one of the best known protein concentrates, widely used in industrialized countries. Due to various price support schemes the latter product is often available at rather low prices.

Several types of crops, apart from oil-seeds, can be used as sources of protein. Gluten and other protein mixtures are obtained from wheat either by extraction methods or air-classification procedures. Other cereals can also be used.

Non-fatty legumes (as distinct from soya and other oil-seed legumes) are potentially important sources of protein concentrates; in the United Kingdom the field bean was used by one firm as a source of textured protein. In most regions of the world some type of non-fatty legume can be grown—for example, the broad bean, *Vicia fava*, is well known as a staple in the Eastern Mediterranean and Middle East regions. Under some circumstances, its use appears to cause some toxic effects, especially in persons susceptible to the disease *favism*. This problem has been studied by the Protein Advisory Group in cooperation with WHO which is encouraging research in a number of countries.

Chlorophyll-rich material (leaves, grasses) can be extracted to give protein concentrates (leaf protein, LPC). Such concentrates, if properly made, contain protein of good biological value, but harvesting and technological problems of processing must be overcome. In manufacturing, one relatively simple process results in a dark green product of a definite taste, which has so far been used only for limited field trials. A more complicated process is required to make a colourless and odourless product, this resulting in a higher price.

Although much of the earlier work has been carried out in the laboratories of research centres, there is now an industrial interest in leaf protein for human consumption by at least one food firm in the United Kingdom and by enterprises in Sweden and Hungary. Work carried out by the Western Regional Research Laboratory of the Department of Agriculture in the USA suggests that by the combined manufacture of a high fibre fraction for use as feed and a protein concentrate, LPC, from alfalfa (lucerne) the concentrate may be sold for feed or even food at lower prices than assumed by the Protein Advisory Group in its Statement No. 11 which discussed economic and other problems associated with LPC.

The report published under the auspices of the International Biological Programme of the Conference at Coimbatore, India, gives an account of work going on in different parts of the world and indicates the two approaches, one the concept of local village-scale production, the other commercial production as proposed in California and in Sweden.

6.6. Current developments in industrialized countries

The production of protein concentrates is now a normal activity of food and related enterprises in many industrialized countries. The uses of the concentrates can be considered under two headings: (i) as components of other foods, and (ii) as the basis of analogue foods.

As components, the protein concentrates are already being widely used; in bread, biscuits and other cereal products; in filled or substitute milks and dairy products; in soup mixes, comminuted meats (e.g. foods of the hamburger type) and in many other prepared foods, including infant and geriatric foods. The study by Hammonds and Call lists many of these uses.

In the analogue foods, the protein isolate or concentrate is produced, as already noted, in forms which somewhat resemble carcass meat, bacon or other commodities. There is no clear border-line between (i) and (ii).

The uses of protein concentrates have often been stimulated by functional advantages (e.g. soya-isolate addition to bread) or by economic benefits, rather than by nutritional considerations. With the increasing use of the new proteins in industrialized countries attention is being given to two aspects of consumer protection, namely health safety in terms of the absence of potentially harmful components, and nutritional value. It is well recognized that in the typical animal food such as milk or meat, the proteins represent only one group of nutrients; other minor but important constituents are present (e.g. vitamins, essential fatty acids and minerals). Procedures have already been agreed in several countries whereby the new protein foods shall be subjected to fortification procedures, supported by appropriate legislation or regulations in regard to composition and labelling, so as to make them equally nutritious as the food or meals they are intended to replace. For instance, milk analogues manufactured from vegetable proteins and vegetable oil should make in all respects the same nutritional contribution as would the same amount of cow's milk.

In industrialized countries commercial production of protein concentrates involve commercial decisions on the choice of raw materials and types of extraction processes. Whereas in the United States soya and cotton-seed are readily available indigenous sources, other countries will have to make decisions depending on whether they wish to be dependent on imports of raw materials (e.g. the soya bean) or partly processed or finished products (e.g. soya isolates and concentrates). In many countries indigenous oil-seeds are available and the objective may then be to develop suitable extraction techniques and to adopt the new extrusion and—less frequently—the spinning techniques to the local materials. The United Kingdom (unlike most countries in continental Europe) has no major indigenous source of oil-seeds; hence the current commercial interest in the field bean, and in leaf protein.

Most chemical undertakings and many food firms owe their success to the full utilization of the by-products from their main manufacturing process and there are many examples of operations where what were considered by-products have become products of considerable commercial value, so that the total operation consists of obtaining several end products from the one series of operations. The commercial cost of any one product to the ultimate consumer then depends on the partition of costs between the different products.

As already seen this principle of preparing several products has been applied to oil-seeds and it can be important in relation to other crops also, as in the current work on alfalfa (lucerne) protein sponsored by the US Department of Agriculture in California.

In the above discussion on current developments in protein concentrates the use of protein from microorganisms or related sources have been omitted from consideration. Once such proteins are in commercial production and cleared from the point of view of health safety for human use, a situation which may not be far off, then the same principles should apply and they will no doubt find their use in a considerable variety of products, cf. Statement No. 4 by the Protein Advisory Group.

7. Protein Foods in Low-Income Countries

7.1. Introduction

The above account of the use of protein preparations in industrialized countries has been given in some detail because, up to recently, many discussions on protein foods have been concerned with their use primarily in the developing world where protein deficiencies are acute. It is important that the low-income countries should be aware that the new products being discussed are not inferior materials, but rather materials that are, or are likely to be, a part of the normal food production and consumption patterns in industrialized countries.

Many of the newer protein concentrates and products are available for export and in that way of potential use in low-income countries, but they are unlikely to make any significant contribution to the protein requirements of people in need in such countries, as their use will be hindered both by distribution problems, price and balance of trade considerations.

Originally, much of the effort in industrialized countries in research and development work on protein concentrates received an impetus from the realization that protein deficiency was common in low-income countries. It was believed that a solution might be found by producing in industrialized countries concentrates which could be supplied to needy low-income populations. Up to comparatively recently two essential matters were often ignored: (1) that population groups have very fixed eating habits and food supply channels and that there are many difficulties in incorporating a protein concentrate into their diet; and (2) even if groups are aware of the benefit which might be derived from the use of such concentrates, the cost in low-income countries is likely to be prohibitive and distribution problems formidable.

Were (1) and (2) not true much wider use could have been made of dry skimmed milk which over several periods has been a surplus commodity, difficult to sell on the world market and readily available in many places at low prices. It appears that for low-income countries protein concentrates are likely to be of use mainly in programmes for food supplies to *groups*, as distinct from domestic consumption.

Reference has already been made to the product SCM. This is relatively inexpensive and has been widely used in emergency feeding where it found ready acceptance by most populations. Yet, even populations which had become accustomed to its use seldom buy it when an emergency programme is terminated, even when supplies are still plentiful.

For low-income countries the best option is presumably in using the protein-containing material *direct* as food rather than in turning it into protein concentrate. As an example may be mentioned the extensive use in Japan of fish hams and fish sausages, both cured communited fish products of high protein value made from human grade trash fish and fish trimmings, which cannot be used directly for foods. Where such direct use is not possible, an indigenous production of protein concentrate, e.g. the manufacture of vegetable protein concentrate for use in substitute milk, may be indicated and has in fact been successful in India.

The potential of the newer protein preparations as meat replacers may depend in part on the possibility of applying spinning and extrusion techniques to indigenous materials in low-income countries to produce products at a low price. Current developments in industrial countries should stimulate activities elsewhere. Progress is delayed in part because of lack of finances and the absence in many areas of any tradition in the agro-based industries and because of shortage also of trained personnel. Also, it must be recognized that at least spinning techniques for obtaining a texturized product are expensive and require heavy capital investment. It is unlikely that these will find widespread use in low-income countries until economic conditions improve.

7.2. Foods for infants and other special groups

The PAG, FAO, UNICEF, UNIDO and other bodies concerned with technical aid recognize that general improvements will depend in large part on the growth of agro-based enterprises, guided by nutritional principles, to improve the food supplies in developing countries. Within the framework of this general problem, is the special and immediate need for protein-rich mixtures suitable as *complete foods* for infants (as human milk-substitutes or as weaning foods) and as *supplementary* foods for other groups (e.g. the pre-school child or nursing mothers).

It was to assist in this limited but important programme that the Protein Advisory Group (PAG) was originally established in 1955 when it was to advise "on safety and acceptability for human consumption of protein-rich food preparations". Most of the considerations in the PAG until the widening of its terms of reference mentioned above were concerned with protein-rich foods obtained from such sources as soya and other oil-seed preparations, and from legumes. The group is still much concerned with this aspect and FAO, WHO as well as bi-lateral organizations follow the procedures for the tests as regards safety and wholesomeness of such products, outlined in Guidelines No. 6 and 7 issued by the Group.

FAO, UNICEF and UNIDO encourage and advise on the production and utilization of such mixtures mainly from indigenous raw materials while WHO deals with matters of nutritional value, health, safety and clinical testing. Outside the United Nations system many organizations, including governments, institutions, foundations and commercial establishments in both industrialized and low-income countries have been involved in some aspects of protein-rich food preparations.

The production of special foods for infants and other groups follow the pattern well known in many high-income countries which have had available throughout this century a variety of commercially produced concentrates, normally milk-based. The problems of low-income countries arise in part because of the non-availability of milk and in part because of the cost of imported products, especially in relationship to the low purchasing power of the groups that are most in need.

The production and use of protein-rich foods in low-income countries may be considered under six headings.

   (i) Choice of protein source
  (ii) Technology of preparation
 (iii) Nutritional fortification
 (iv) Guidelines for safety
  (v) Clinical testing
 (vi) Acceptability, distribution and marketing
(vii) Economics and finance.

These points will now be discussed in turn. The notes which follow are summaries of the extensive documentation produced by the Protein Advisory Group, its sponsoring and associated agencies and other bodies. Recent publications include a study (1972) on protein-rich mixtures, carried out by the Tropical Products Institute at the request of the Protein Advisory Group.

7.3. Sources of protein mixtures

There is now general agreement that for economic and other reasons the aim must be the production of protein-rich foods *within* the developing country or region, and efforts in the immediate future should be directed towards the use of components which can be derived from *indigenous* crops, or from crops that can readily be introduced into local agricultural systems. In practice this means that basic constituents will normally be derived from oil-seeds and/or legumes (some oil-seeds such as soya and groundnuts are in fact legumes), supplemented by cereals and other plant produce. The use of edible fish flour (or some other animal product) is not excluded, if this can be produced locally; other sources (e.g. leaf protein) may be of use later if improvements in processing methods and cost reduction is achieved.

It seems unlikely that the necessary proteins will be available at economic prices if the foods as a whole, or major components have to be imported from outside the region. The use of imported milk powder as a component should not be excluded however, especially if there is a reasonable chance that a local dairy industry is likely to grow and to supply future needs.

7.4. Technology of preparation

Considerable experience has been gained in several low-income countries in the preparation, marketing and use of protein-rich foods. This experience has had as its background research and development work in North America and in Europe. The newer extrusion and related techniques are used in the preparation of some mixtures prepared to specifications for distribution by UNICEF, WFP and other aid agencies to low-income countries. The problem now before many developing countries is to implement local production.

7.5. Nutritional fortification

The typical protein-rich food contains fats, carbohydrates and other components in addition to protein. As mentioned elsewhere the addition of minor components such as trace elements, vitamins and related factors is an important part of the preparation of any complete food and such additions are especially necessary with preparations from plant proteins, preparations which may be deficient because of absence of minor nutrients in the source material or because of removal during processing. The empirical rule for milk substitutes is to ensure the inclusion by fortification of all the known minor constituents of human milk. Evidence is available, through WHO and FAO and also through reports from local or regional institutes as far apart as Guatemala and India, that oil-seed legumes/cereal preparations, suitably reinforced with minor components, are adequate from a nutritional standpoint. Detailed recommendations for fortification have now been worked out by various national and international bodies. The Protein Advisory Group has in its Statement No. 6 recommended that all dried skimmed milk is fortified with vitamins A and D when used in feeding programmes in low-income countries.

7.6. Guidelines for safety

As already noted oil-seeds, and other protein sources may contain toxic or anti-nutritional components which must be removed or destroyed if the material is to be used for foods especially if those foods are to be used by children. There is also the possibility of toxic factors being introduced during processing unless conditions and materials, for example, solvents and emulsifiers, are rigidly controlled. A third hazard arises from mycotoxins (e.g. from mouldy groundnuts) which seem to be extremely poisonous in small amounts and which may develop during the harvest and post-harvest period of storage of various plant products.

Reports on the health safety of oil-seed based and other protein foods have been prepared for review by the Protein Advisory Group. In addition a series of detailed guidelines have been issued. The Group's guidelines, recommendations and statements are listed in the bibliography. These documents deal with different protein sources and cover industrial preparations and methods for testing preparations for toxic materials. They contain essential reference material, important for government agencies and industrial enterprises concerned with specific sources of protein and different types of products.

Reference may particularly be made to PAG Statement No. 2 on alfatoxins and to PAG Guideline No. 2 for preparing food quality groundnut flour, No. 4 for preparation of edible cotton-seed protein concentrate, No. 5 for edible soya grits and flour, and No. 14 on defatted edible sesame flour.

7.7. Clinical testing

WHO considers it essential that new food preparations be tested prior to their use and the Protein Advisory Group has issued guidelines on laboratory as well as clinical testing. The clinical testing of new protein foods is by no means easy. Extensive experience has been gained at the Institute of Nutrition of Central America and Panama (INCAP) and elsewhere. WHO has made cooperative arrangements with several centres at which facilities are available for testing such new preparations. Full details are given in WHO reports, which show that various preparations in active use are nutritionally adequate in terms of biochemical analysis and animal feeding tests and are nutritionally effective in the prevention and treatment of protein-calorie malnutrition.

In these tests, the material first undergoes a pre-clinical trial in accordance with the Protein Advisory Group's Guideline No. 6. Subsequently, it is tested clinically in the various centres with which WHO collaborates, following PAG Guideline No. 7.

7.8. Acceptability, distribution and marketing

The marketing of new products in low-income countries presents many difficulties; such plans must be worked out country by country in accordance with local food habits and traditions. The study of the local situation calls for a multi-disciplinary effort, beginning with social anthropology, extending to psychological and sociological studies, and leading to the application of food promotion and marketing techniques. Marketing and associated problems are discussed in recent reports from FAO. The staff of FAO includes specialists in food promotion activities and a body of information is being collected from which should emerge general principles of action, to be applied with appropriate modifications in different countries or regions.

The Protein Advisory Group has prepared its Statement No. 5 and an extensive Guideline No. 10 giving detailed suggestions on marketing approaches.

7.9. Economics and finance

Questions of economics and finance are central to the provision of protein-rich foods. If these are to reach vulnerable groups they must be available in adequate quantity at low cost. It has become evident in many countries that if local factories are to be established subsidies in some form will be required, especially in the initial "take-off period". How these subsidies are to be arranged (for example through guaranteed purchases) is a question that must be decided on a local or national basis, but there is now a body of experience on which to draw. Some of this has been summarized in reports already mentioned, namely the study by the Tropical Products Institute and PAG Guideline No. 10.

7.10. Preparations now in use

The above points (7.3 to 7.9) apply with suitable modifications to a wide range of preparations in different countries.

In practice a number of preparations are now being used although often on a very limited scale, in different countries. Some of the preparations are based on moderately complicated protein extracts; others on relatively simple processing techniques. The range of products is illustrated by the following four examples (further details of which are given in the report from the Tropical Products Institute).

Incaparina is made in accordance with several different formulae, one is a mixture of cotton-seed flour (38%), maize flour (58%), torula yeast (3%) and vitamins and calcium supplements. The cotton-seed flour is sometimes replaced by a mixture of cotton-seed and soya flour.

Spray dried protein food produced by the Central Food Technology Research Institute in Mysore, India (multi-purpose food MPF), and includes wheat flour (65%), a ground nut isolate (25%), skimmed milk powder (10%) with mineral and vitamin additions.

Superamine (Algeria) is also manufactured according to different formulae, one such includes hard wheat flour (28%), chick-pea and lentil flour (56%) and milk powder (10%), also appropriately fortified.

Pro-Nutro (South Africa) is composed of yellow and white maize together with whole fat soya bean and groundnut, whey powder, food yeast and other supplements.

PART II

LINES OF ACTION

8. National Food and Nutrition Policies

8.1. Relationships: food—agriculture—public health

It has long been recognized that nutrition problems can be treated successfully only on an inter-disciplinary basis and will in any one country be the concern of different ministries and government agencies.

Some thirty-five years ago the League of Nations established a *Mixed Committee* to examine and report on the relationship of nutrition and "health, agriculture and economic policy". The Committee was *mixed* in respect to academic disciplines and professional experience as well as in its geographical membership; its meeting brought together economists and statisticians, agricultural scientists and practitioners, medical scientists and public health officers. It was during the Assembly debates on the work of the Mixed Committee that the Australian statesman, Lord Bruce, first used the phrase "the marriage of health and agriculture" as a key to nutrition, a phrase that provided inspiration to nutrition workers in many countries and was echoed at the Hot Springs Conference in 1944 and the Quebec Conference in 1945 when it was embodied in the philosophy of FAO, the Food and Agriculture Organisation of the United Nations, which was founded at that conference.

This concept of close cooperation between health and agriculture is central to the policy of both FAO and WHO. Although the desirability of such a policy is also widely accepted in national governments, much remains to be done—especially in low-income countries—to make the cooperation effective and fruitful. Methods of initiating and executing national food and nutritional policies have been considered in detail in several publications including the report of the 1961 Geneva Meeting of the Joint FAO/WHO Committee on Nutrition and more recently in the FAO *Manual on Food and Nutrition Policy*, published in 1969.

8.2. Implementation of policy

In looking at national policies it is convenient to distinguish between three types of programmes:

(i)   those that will normally lie within the province of a Ministry of Health to be implemented by medical and para-medical personnel;

(ii) those that fall within the province of the Ministry of Food and Agriculture (or of separate Ministries of Food and of Agriculture in ccoperation with the agricultural industries and agricultural scientists, and preferably also with the food industries and food scientists. (Very often other ministries, apart from Agriculture and/or Food—for example, Ministries of Trade, Commerce or Industry—are concerned with food industries);

(iii) those which may involve the above ministries and others concerned with education, social welfare or other areas.

Some of the main activities in the above categories are outlined in the following sections.

8.3. Health programmes

The objectives should be to relate medical activities and public health legislation and services to the nutritional needs of the human population. Such programmes normally include the following:

(i)   epidemiological studies, including clinical surveys, to determine the magnitude and nature of nutritional problems;

(ii) establishment of nutrient requirements for vulnerable and diseased groups;

(iii) implementation of measures by medical, public health and auxiliary personnel for the reduction of malnutrition;

(iv) development of adequate dietetic services in hospitals and welfare institutions;

(v)   evaluation of the interaction between improper feeding and other causes of diseases; and

(vi) advising other governmental agencies on the public health aspects of nutrition problems with which they may be concerned.

8.4. Food and agricultural programmes

Food and agricultural programmes are required to relate the production, processing, handling and consumption of food to nutritional needs. The following may be included:

  (i) assessment of national food supplies and consumption levels in relation to the nutritional needs of the population;
 (ii) establishment of short-term and long-term targets for food production and supplies, taking into account the nutritional needs of the population and the agricultural, economic and social factors affecting food production and consumption;
(iii) provision of technical advice on different aspects of agricultural production and also on methods of storage, preservation, processing, transport and marketing of food to avoid waste and to maintain maximum nutritive values;
(iv) collection and dissemination of information on the nutritive value of processed and unprocessed foods and the effects on nutritive value of common commercial or household processing practices;
 (v) action in respect of food control and legislation so as to help ensure the quality of food, including its maximum nutritional value and wholesomeness. In this, consideration must be given to problems of enforcement and review. It may be futile to enact laws when compliance cannot be enforced; regulations which are not frequently reviewed may hinder rather than further an effective food supply.

8.5. General and cooperative programmes

Other lines of action involving potentially two or more Ministries or governmental agencies with other bodies such as universities and research institutes are the following:

  (i) Steps to meet the needs of special groups through supplementary and general group-feeding programmes for hospitals and other institutions, schools, workers and others.
 (ii) The periodic assessment of levels of food consumption and of nutritional status.
(iii) Food and nutrition education and training programmes at different levels, within the formal education and through adult education and extension channels.
(iv) Research and experimental work on food and nutrition problems.

8.6. Coordination of policy

The Report of the 1961 FAO/WHO Joint Committee on Nutrition repeated earlier proposals for the coordination of national policy. It noted that "by their very nature, many problems in nutrition are the concern of two or more ministries or government departments. Thus, while much may be achieved by personal and technical cooperation between officers of ministries of, for example, health and agriculture, experience has shown that, in many countries, special machinery for coordination of national efforts may be both necessary and desirable."

It was suggested that "this coordination should embrace not only ministries directly concerned with nutrition, but others such as those concerned with economic development, which may require advice on nutritional matters because they may be responsible for major policy decisions, e.g. in respect of food imports and exports or the establishment of new industries". The Committee noted also that "the plan of cooperation and coordination may also involve ministries (or departments) responsible for education, social welfare, economic affairs and community development, and not least, governmental or public bodies concerned with universities and/or medical and agricultural education and research."

Because of the above considerations, it has been considered wise in several countries to establish a national body, under a title such as "National Food and Nutrition Council", charged with the tasks of:

(i) advising the government as a whole in food and nutrition problems and on the desirable action to be taken; and

(ii) securing agreement on the ways and means through which national programmes can be implemented, whether through the different individual ministries, or through the secretariat of the council, or through other bodies, e.g. teaching or research centres.

The 1961 report further noted that "in many countries the formulation of integrated nutrition programmes will not be possible unless such interministerial and interdepartmental coordination is affected by a statutory body with access to, and with powers to advise, the highest authorities of government".

In spite of the obvious advantage of national food and nutrition councils, it appears that relatively few countries have been able to set them up on a permanent basis. Some of the barriers to the establishment of these national bodies are well known in industrialized countries, namely (i) difficulties in getting people in different academic disciplines to work together and to understand the terminology, jargon and concepts of other disciplines, (ii) problems in securing cooperation between government departments, in particular the tendency of some one department to try to act as "overlord" so that interdepartmental committees lose their original form and become appendices of one ministry with a loss of commitment on the part of the other ministries concerned.

In developing countries other bottlenecks arise from shortage of personnel and reluctance of ministries to release key personnel for seemingly unproductive interdepartmental meetings. In some countries there may be an officer of the ministry of health with knowledge and appreciation of nutritional problems, but no-one with adequate nutritional knowledge in the ministry of agriculture. The effective functioning of a food and nutrition council depends very much on the work carried out by its secretariat between meetings and experienced personnel capable of correlating nutrition and economic factors are not readily available.

Because of such difficulties, experience even in those countries where national food and nutrition councils have been established has not always been encouraging. Often such bodies meet too seldom to accomplish much; more often their advice is not heeded. In any one country nutrition programmes usually yield less *obvious* results than other economic development activities, e.g. road building and irrigation; therefore they often receive a low priority. Moreover it is often difficult to point to one specific action which will improve nutrition. Advisers often have to recommend several different, even if related, actions; the policy planner or politician who cannot see a clear goal or a prospect of speedy results may turn his interest to other, more well-defined areas. Low-income countries are beset with so many needs for development activities, there is often a shortage of trained personnel; the administrative machinery may be weak. As a consequence of the above, nutrition problems are often not accorded sufficiently high priority and, even when they are accepted in principle, funding may be insufficient and the administrative system may be incapable of coping with nutritional programmes which are almost of necessity complex in nature.

8.7. Problems relating to ministries of agriculture

Not only have difficulties been found in securing interministerial cooperation, but there are also problems in many countries in relation to the objectives and scope of the ministry of agriculture. In some countries there is a ministry of food parallel to the ministry of agriculture; this formula can work well providing functions are well defined. In other countries the ministry of agriculture may have a vague responsibility to deal with post-harvest problems, without having the necessary authority or staff. When a ministry of agriculture is responsible both for agricultural production and food supplies, there are clearly advantages if the word *Food* is joined to *Agriculture* in the title of the ministry.

It is unfortunate that ministries of agriculture (in countries where no ministry of food exists) often follow the older European pattern of limiting activities to "within the farmgate". Under such circumstances there may be no agency of government to stimulate interest in food preservation and processing problems, and food production itself may suffer because of an excessive concentration in agriculture on cash crops.

In a few countries there are further problems because following independence older administrative formulae have been followed in which the ministry of agriculture is limited largely to *crop production*, whereas *animal production* and associated veterinary services come within the province of some parallel ministry.

While it is true that many different types of governmental organization can function effectively, the result of some patterns in low-income countries is a situation in which no senior minister is concerned with food. Such a situation may be relatively unimportant in an affluent industrialized country where food industries are well established and where a variety of scientific and technical bodies is concerned with food and nutrition. In a developing country the lack of a minister with specific responsibilities may be the main limiting factor hindering food and nutritional improvement.

Thus, while recognizing the very real advances of recent years, the 1967 Conference of FAO felt the need to re-affirm older policies: "The Conference agreed that close liaison between nutritionists and agriculturists was essential in the planning of food supplies and improved food production and consumption levels. The attainment of this liaison, however, was often hampered by the absence of the necessary technical units and of the organization and administrative framework in ministries of agriculture. It was felt that the creation of units responsible for food and nutrition in ministries of agriculture could help bring about the desired closer association between nutritionists and agriculturists, as had been achieved in a number of countries. Such units could collect information on the food and nutrition situation that was required as a basis for food production planning and overall economic and social planning. The Conference also recognized that machinery should be developed to ensure coordination between the activities of all ministries and departments dealing with human nutrition, including the planning authorities".

8.8. Food and nutrition in relation to economic development

A recent conference organized by the Dag Hammarskjöld Foundation in Sweden in 1971 discussed *Nutrition as a Priority in African Development* and brought to the surface problems that have been considered at intervals by United Nations Agencies and other groups for many years. The problems can be stated simply. There may be in a particular country a group in the ministry of health, a second group in the ministry of agriculture, and perhaps even a third group in the ministry of education interested in nutrition problems and anxious to initiate or expand constructive programmes. However, all such programmes require an allocation of state resources and in some cases requests to technical assistance agencies. Ultimately decisions have to be made at political level within a cabinet or a parliament, where the deciding voice may come from ministries of finance or economic planning or their equivalent.

Such problems go far beyond Africa. They occur in all low-income countries and, indeed, in industrialized countries as well. The important question is "how can specialists in economics and planning be convinced that a food and nutrition policy is important and deserves an adequate allocation of national resources?" Similar problems of allocation of national finance occur within ministries. Thus in health the type of question is "what proportion of a budget should be spent on nutrition and other aspects of preventive medicine, as distinct from the provision of new hospitals which may serve prestige (and local political) as well as health purposes?" In agriculture, the familiar question is "How far should we worry about food crops, their preservation and utilization; why not devote our resources to the production and marketing of cash crops, and assume that we will then be able to buy the food we want?"

The problem in its broadest context was discussed at a conference on *Nutrition in National Planning* at the Massachusetts Institute of Technology in 1971; the report, Scrimshaw (1973), was used as a background paper for the Protein Advisory Group in the summer of 1973.

These and similar questions are an inevitable part of the decision-making process and answers must be found both on the basis of general principle and in terms of the local situation. The UN Agencies have been aware of the difficulties for many years, but it is now evident that steps should be taken in at least four directions:

(i) to collect information about the cost of malnutrition in terms of public health;

(ii) to assess other social and economic losses arising from malnutrition;

(iii) to draw attention to the experience of countries that have successfully made an investment in food and nutrition; and

(iv) to devise ways and means to promote greater contacts (in any one country or in a region) between those professionally concerned with food and nutrition problems and others concerned primarily with economics, statistics and planning.

9. Action within Low-Income Countries

9.1. Proteins in relation to general food and nutrition policy

In the preceding chapter, the emphasis has been given to *general* food policies rather than to *protein* questions as such. The governments in any one country should be encouraged to recognize the contribution of a sound food and nutrition policy to national development and then to apply these policies in practice to ensure that the needs also for protein are taken fully into account. Next to insufficient calorie supplies, lack of protein is almost certainly the major nutritional problem in many countries, but the solution may lie in overall improvements in agronomy and animal production and a more effective distribution system.

The policy to be adopted in any one country will depend in part on the existing local food situation and in particular (a) whether the production of milk, eggs or meat is possible and is likely to increase; (b) whether the staple plant foodstuffs are cereals which supply a reasonable amount of protein; (c) whether the staple is cassava or other crops low in protein.

In countries (a) and (b) the primary objective will be to increase the total amounts of food available, so that increased protein levels in the diet can be obtained. In countries (c) special efforts may be required to encourage also the production and use of cereals and legumes. In most countries some gains could probably be achieved by the introduction of high protein varieties of crops.

In the remainder of this chapter an attempt is made to select certain lines of activity which appear to be of importance both in relation to a general nutrition policy and more specifically in relation to protein. It is impossible to cover all facets of agricultural development and food marketing, or to record the many advances in agricultural practices and extension methods over the past few decades. The selection is made on the basis of areas of activity which appear to be in whole or part neglected, as distinct from more traditional aspects of agricultural and food development which are often well understood.

9.2. Transitional stages of development

Proposals for new agricultural or nutritional programmes must be examined in different countries in terms of the actual stages of industrial and agricultural development already reached. It is becoming recognized that the distinction between *industrialized* (or *high-income*) and *developing* (or *low-income*) countries can only be a rough guide. Some authors now prefer a three-fold category—to include in the centre *transitional* countries, which have built up over the years an infrastructure of education at different levels, research institutes and industry, even though the major part of the population is still living on a low income. In the UN usage, a fourth group emerges, namely that of the *very low-income* group of countries.

Countries such as India and Argentina have a range of chemical and other industries and are able to proceed rapidly with certain types of programme which may be quite impossible elsewhere. Thus, an agricultural development programme based on high yielding varieties which in turn demands high inputs of fertilisers may be possible in India, a country with an organized chemical industry but not in some others. The same considerations apply to proposals for the production of microbial protein; such production depends on an input of ammonia (or equivalent) to provide the nitrogen for the protein synthesis, and the ability to establish and maintain a relatively complex chemical process industry.

All the proposals noted in this chapter have to be examined critically in the light of local circumstances. None of the proposals can be regarded as new; several, in fact, are mentioned by different countries in their reports to the United Nations following the request of the Secretary General to report programmes and progress in regard to protein supplies and summarized in *The Protein Problem* (1968).

9.3. Crop production

In all current plans for increased protein from agronomy, there should be a triple objective at the production stage, namely better yields, more efficient harvesting, and avoidance of waste through crop disease. Increased production requires increased farm inputs, such as irrigation, farm equipment, fertilisers and crop protection chemicals. There are corresponding objectives for land animals and fisheries. In most low-income countries, the older agricultural research and development institutes were established primarily for cash crops and the trained personnel available may have had little experience in food crop production. It is clearly important that encouragement is given to increased production of food crops and that ministries examine production data, and proposals for future action, in terms of the *nutritional quality*, including protein content, of the final produce as well as in relation to *total yields.*

Under the auspices of the Protein Advisory Group, and with support from many international and bi-lateral agencies and the Ford and the Rockefeller Foundations, a meeting on promoting and improving legumes, as a protein-rich type of crop was held in Rome in 1972. The proceedings have been published; a summary of conclusions is given in the PAG Statement No. 22. The meeting was considered highly useful in that it provided an opportunity for plant breeders, biochemists, nutritionists and economists to consider the subject jointly, and because it focused attention on the need for guiding food crop production in the direction of protein-rich crops.

9.4. Animal production

Typical of the problems that require discussion and decisions in several developing countries is the extent of the capital investment and national effort that should be placed on protein production from *animal* as distinct from *crop* sources. The general information in the scientific literature on this matter is based largely on data obtained in industrialized countries on the efficiency of food conversion and the cost of animal feeding stuffs; more precise information is required in developing countries.

Attention must be given to the fact that in the commercial production of veal, pork, poultry meat or milk, 7 to 8kg of protein in the feed produce 1 kg of animal protein. In low-income countries, the feed protein is likely to be of vegetable origin, but if the conversion rate is so low, we must consider carefully if means cannot be found to utilize the vegetable protein direct for human food, rather than for feed. As an example, development efforts are often directed towards establishing milk production in areas where none have existed and where no tradition exists for giving milk to young children. The question arises: would it not be better to stimulate some production of vegetable-based protein-rich foods of the type mentioned above, with a consequent more efficient use of available protein supplies?

There is, however, another aspect of this problem; namely, the large stocks of domesticated animals in many parts of the developing world. Thus, Africa in 1970 possessed 97 million cows and produced

41 million metric tons of milk. Europe possessed 108 million cows and produced 178 million tons of milk a year, i.e. about eight times as much per animal. Similarly, the yield in meat in kilo per animal was 60 for beef/veal in Europe and 14 in Africa. For pork yield was 80 kilo per animal in Europe and 41 in Africa. These figures indicate that there is room for very substantially increased supplies from those domestic animals which are already in existence, which already use the feed or grassland, but which are not nearly as productive as appears possible.

All types of animal (including fisheries) production can contribute directly to protein supplies but policy decisions are required on the types of animals to be used for meat and/or milk production and the sources and cost of feeding stuffs. The potential advantages of ruminants are well known, they can make use of plant material which, for reason of high harvest cost and high fibre content, cannot be used directly by man, and they may utilize also non-agricultural sources of nitrogen. Mono-gastric animals such as pigs and chickens compete in their protein need in some measure with man, but swine and poultry are often kept around human dwellings and feed mostly on waste from the household. Under these circumstances they make use of otherwise wasted food supplies and become also useful suppliers of animal protein without reducing already scarce food resources.

Often in development programmes, the emphasis has been on the *large* domesticated animal, rather than on the smaller animal, which may have higher efficiency as a converter of feed. In recent years a rapid increase in chicken production has taken place in North America and Northern Europe, and several countries at different stages of development (e.g. Israel, Lebanon and Singapore) have built up chicken farms which contribute both meat and eggs at prices which are competitive with other animal protein sources. Elsewhere, efforts are being made (e.g. through village cooperatives) to make more extensive use of other small animals (e.g. the rabbit and guinea pig). These have been used by schools and other institutions, but have rarely received the attention as a potential protein supply which they may deserve.

In most low-income countries programmes for milk production have been based on traditions from the industrialized countries, i.e. the use of the dairy cow. In India, however, the water buffalo has been successfully used for milk production and the sheep and the goat are traditional sources of dairy products in North Africa and the Middle East. Such animals may make an important contribution to protein supplies at the domestic, or village or institutional level, even if considered only as a transition stage to the development of a dairy industry based on larger animals. They can be looked after by women or children without undue difficulty and, in the absence of an organized milk industry, can well be used for supplies to childrens' hospitals or clinics.

In some countries a bottleneck in animal production (e.g. in chicken farming) is the relatively high cost of animal feed. There is room for further development of local animal feed industries based on indigenous raw materials.

A further general problem retarding animal production in some regions arises from the over-rigid separation of governmental departments concerned with agronomy and animal production and the lack of senior personnel with expertise in animal *production* as distinct from animal *disease*.

9.5. Kitchen gardens and allotments

Comparatively few papers on development policy refer to food production by private individuals and families as part-time, leisure-time activities in kitchen gardens, "home gardens" or "allotments". Such activities are widely practised in Europe.

An official report on this subject published in the United Kingdom includes surveys of the position in various European countries and gives an account of the contributions from home gardens in the United Kingdom during World War II, when home food production reached the stage in 1944 of supplying about 10% of total (home) agricultural food production. In addition to vegetable produce, small animal keeping was encouraged with consequent improvements in protein supplies. Success was achieved in part because of active government support—through measures such as the allocation of land, supplies of seed and animal feed.

The Nutrition Division, now the Food Policy and Nutrition Division, of FAO, in conjunction with UNICEF, has for many years encouraged school and community garden projects, but these have not always received adequate support at government level. It is suggested that this matter should be re-examined in a wider context with a stress on the importance (a) of encouraging local personal and private initiative, (b) of a government or local authority taking appropriate action to allocate land, especially in urban areas.

When we consider the extent of protein deficiency—and of food generally—we cannot ignore the possibility of a sizeable production outside *organized agriculture*. This additional source of food could be particularly important because of the increasing degree of urbanization which is a characteristic of so many regions. Small-scale production is, of course, widely practised in some low-income countries. If this is to be extended, close cooperation will be required between agricultural groups and groups responsible for urban planning and for local government. In some countries, home gardens would have advantages which go beyond the food supply in providing occupation in times of unemployment or under-employment.

9.6. Food losses

Food losses and their prevention, i.e. the "War on Waste" is now accepted as an important means of increasing the available food supplies. Waste can occur at different points:

   (i) in the field due to losses of growing crops (or corresponding losses because of animal disease);

  (ii) at the harvest and post-harvest stage during storage and transport;

 (iii) during processing; and

 (iv) in the home.

From the replies provided by different countries to the Secretary General's questionnaire in 1968 and from FAO reports, it is evident that the importance of losses in stage (i) are widely recognized and that a considerable and increasing scientific and technical effort is being put into crop protection and the irradication of crop disease, and also into the prevention and treatment of animal disease.

Much less attention is given to post-harvest losses which can be very high in countries in tropical and semi-tropical regions where a combination of heat and humidity, and insects and pests of many types, lead to very rapid deterioration of stored food. This problem is not limited to grain storage; it affects all commodities and in particular animal produce; it requires application of many aspects of food science, technology, and engineering. In most low-income countries further and more concentrated efforts are required in relation to post-harvest problems.

9.7. The role of the food industries

There is scope in many developing countries for the improvement of traditional methods of processing and also for the establishment of modern food industries. Some modern large-scale food factories have been successfully established in India, Pakistan and other parts of Asia and in some countries in Central and South America and Africa.

In many cases, however, failures have been common with heavy financial losses to governments as well as to private investors. The cause of these failures are complex. A primary reason may be the absence of local personnel with industrial and food industry experience who can evaluate project proposals and/or manage factories where they are established. Mistakes have often been made by persons who oversimplify the problems of food processing, for example the graduate in agriculture with no industrial experience or the graduate in engineering who is not used to dealing with agricultural raw materials.

Errors have been made in such seemingly obvious matters as:

  (i) the siting of a factory without provision for adequate supplies of the agricultural raw materials—or for supplies of water, an essential component in food operations;

 (ii) lack of provision for agricultural materials of the right type for processing;

(iii) incorrect decisions on the size of the establishment and types of equipment;

(iv) lack of knowledge about distribution and marketing, or overall management.

The solution to some of these problems can come only through adequate education and training schemes and through technical advisory services.

9.8. Scale of development: appropriate technology

One question to be resolved in many countries is the type and size of industrial processing units to be planned. In some countries and with some types of raw materials, there may be strong and valid arguments for large scale units of the type common in industrialized countries. There may be other circumstances in which it would be better to establish small scale units to provide cottage or village industries. Thus, the modern capital-intensive industry may be inefficient in the absence of experienced technical and general management and may provide little employment, whereas the smaller labour-intensive unit, which can be established in small towns may supply useful employment and counteract the population drift towards large towns.

Several low-income countries have begun to discuss the problem; others have gone further and are taking steps to apply the concept of *appropriate technology*. Difficulties are often experienced in obtaining technical advice, including advice about suitable equipment. The frequent reliance on technical specialists from the industrialized countries create difficulties in this area. The foreign specialist normally has little or no experience with other technologies than those in use in his own country; in fact, a new technology will often have to be developed which cannot be copied from any existing practice.

9.9. Protein-rich food preparations

The question of the *concentration* of protein is all important for children, for whom in the absence of milk some protein-rich preparation is essential. Protein-rich preparations are desirable for other groups also. Various possibilities have to be considered. Protein nutrition may be improved through improved milk supplies, or by improved meal preparations in the homes. Improvement may also be possible through the establishment of a production of a protein-rich food mixture.

The main problems central to any project for the establishment of a production and distribution unit for a protein-rich food in any country can be considered under three headings (i) the formulation of mixtures based on available (or potentially available) raw materials, (ii) the building, equipping and operating of a factory, (iii) marketing and distribution. The experience gained by the UN Agencies and other bodies suggests that (i) can usually be solved fairly readily; in respect to (iii) much experience has been gained, especially as a result of surveys and promotion studies carried out by FAO. The technical problems associated with (ii) can be dealt with through sound technical advice. There are, however, in respect to both (i) and (ii) serious financial problems in particular how to finance the establishment and the early stages of a production and how to ensure that products are in fact available for those in need.

Theoretically the *organization* of a factory could be undertaken if a local government so wishes, by a food firm from an industrialized country. In practice there have been very few cases where this has been successful, but the possibility is worth further study. It would clearly be useful if prototype factories could be established in a limited number of countries. Assuming finance were available, FAO, in association with other bodies, could work out plans and specifications and costs with provision for management and technical staff over an agreed initial period, possibly five years. Once a beginning was made by the United Nations system for prototype projects, national agencies and foundations might well agree to participate in sponsorship.

The second financial problem concerns the *distribution* to individuals in need, as distinct from those able to purchase foods on the open market. Some plan of guaranteed purchases for an initial period is necessary, and the local government could well be expected to give some assistance. Voluntary bodies in industrialized countries might be willing to assist with grants for such guaranteed purchases over an initial period.

Parallel to the above programme there would be scope for continuing studies on food acceptability and formulations of different types, ranging from protein drinks to high protein breads and other cereal products.

Experience has shown that it is very difficult to establish a market for protein-rich weaning food or general type food through the regular commercial channels; the food may be four times as expensive per unit of weight as the lowest cost of staple sold through the traditional channels. Therefore, a very effective promotional effort is required to convince low-income groups that they should pay what for them is a very high price for a food.

The Protein Advisory Group at its 20th meeting made some recommendations on processed weaning foods projects for low-income countries. Although programmes for the commercial production of weaning foods developed in low-income countries do not normally reach large numbers of needy children, it is worth noting that *free* distribution of such foods, not only dried skimmed milk but also vegetable preparations, have been quite extensive. Products such as CSM, a commercially produced weaning food consisting of corn (maize) flour, soya flour and dried milk mixture, fortified with vitamins and minerals, reached by 1973 a total production figure of about 2 million tons. It appears that the free distribution of this product may result in some, although as yet very limited, commercial sale in some low-income countries.

9.10. Food processing and development centres: technical advisory work

The United Nations' Development Programme (UNDP) has sponsored in cooperation with FAO a limited number of food research and development institutes, which supplement the work of the relatively large number of agricultural centres in existence. Some other UNDP/UNIDO and ILO projects also have a food component. Additional requests are coming from governments.

Such food institutes can serve as advisory centres for new food enterprises. Their success in relation to nutrition will depend, however, on how far a multi-disciplinary, as distinct from a more narrow technical, approach can be followed. The technical approach is all important to achieve efficient production, but in low-income countries it is essential that nutritional objectives be stressed and nutritional guidance made available. It is desirable also that centres recruit staff (and, in the initial stage, advisers) who are interested in and competent in economics, statistics and marketing, and in questions of food acceptability and food promotion. It is equally important that provision is made for effective contact with the local industry and trade, and that training programmes are encouraged.

Under the sponsorship of the Protein Advisory Group a survey was carried out of some such centres and their performance. The general conclusion was that some projects might well benefit from a narrowing (or sharpening) of their objectives with improved nutrition accepted as an important economic, as well as humanitarian, target. One question that might well be discussed is how far existing projects or new projects for food processing and development centres could embody on a temporary (for example, five year) basis, a production section. In considering this, one may well recall that the production of special foods for infants in industrialized countries was in the initial stages, at the beginning of the present century, sponsored through pharmaceutical rather than through food enterprises.

There is some analogy between the current problems of initiating protein-food production enterprises and corresponding problems in Europe one hundred years ago following the work of Pasteur and the recognition of the importance of the production of sera and vaccines. The Pasteur Institute in Paris and corresponding centres in other countries were established not only to undertake fundamental and applied research in relation to Pasteur's discoveries, but also to produce vaccines at a time when pharmaceutical enterprises were reluctant to embark on production programmes for such new and in part controversial products.

Such an approach to the protein food programme might be followed (as indeed it has been in Guatemala and parts of India) with the understanding that the production activities were intended to deal with current emergencies and to stimulate wider industrial programmes.

On the initiative of the World Bank, IBRD, a consultative group has been established, in which FAO, IBRD, bi-lateral aid-organizations and the Ford Foundation and the Rockefeller Foundation cooperate with the aim to coordinate, guide, encourage and finance agricultural research in the developing world. A number of research institutes of considerable size and actual or potential impact receive support from this group. It is to be hoped that the group will accept as its mandate not only improvement in agricultural production but also in processing, and marketing since no agricultural production can succeed without an efficient outlet, i.e. appropriate storage, transport, processing and marketing.

One subject has been discussed in the Consultative Group which merits special attention. The research and development institutes under its auspicies are sufficiently large to have a multidisciplinary staff. Their problem is, through field stations and advisory work, to obtain the necessary dissemination of results over a wide area, i.e. "outreach". On the other hand, smaller institutes and more specific-ally national institutes in low-income nations, can benefit from contacts with larger research and development establishments, often in the developed world, e.g. through "link" schemes (see page 99).

9.11. Education and training

The report of the UN Advisory Committee on the Application of Science and Technology to Development (ACAST, 1968) and also the UN Secretary-General's Report on Proteins (1968) have drawn attention to the need for trained personnel to implement a protein policy as part of overall food and nutrition policies. In developing countries there is frequently a shortage of indigenous people trained in medicine and agriculture, but in most countries there is an even greater shortage (sometimes a complete absence) of people with training in, knowledge about, and experience with post-harvest problems. The gaps occur both at university (graduate) level and at technical level.

Personnel are required for a variety of posts in the ministries of agriculture and/or food, and other ministries, for food analysis and control laboratories, for research and development work and for industrial food-enterprises. The deficiencies cover several related areas: food science, nutrition, and home economics. The shortage of personnel is especially obvious in countries which are endeavouring to start industrial food enterprises.

On a temporary basis assistance can be given through field specialists from the United Nations system or bi-lateral agencies. Fellowship schemes for the training of personnel from low-income countries in food science and food processing may also be helpful. A very considerable expansion in such fellowships is required with a critical review of the actual type of programme, so that *training for practical work* (as distinct from theoretical research) receives full emphasis.

Because of the numbers likely to be required for food activities, developing countries will not be able to solve their problems until they have available within their own boundaries or nearby countries training centres at the university level together with other centres at the sub-university level for technicians and craftsmen in this field.

It is suggested, therefore, that renewed efforts be made by FAO and other bodies concerned within the United Nations system, and by other aid agencies, to assist in the establishment of university (or equivalent) departments to provide courses in food and nutrition science, food marketing, management, and related subjects. Progress has been made in some parts of Asia and in South America, but it appears that in tropical Africa there are at present only two university departments offering undergraduate courses in food science and/or technology. The first of these (in Ghana) was established in 1961 following proposals from FAO. The second (at the University of Ife, Nigeria) is "linked" to the Food Science Department at the University of Reading.

Several universities in English speaking and French speaking tropical Africa and also in the Near East are anxious to establish food departments, but delays have occured because of the difficulties in obtaining external financial aid. Whereas food and/or nutrition departments are well established in North America and the Soviet Union, they are relatively uncommon in Western Europe. This may be one reason why many advisers have overlooked the desirability of establishing such departments which may be essential to the progress of the agro-based industries. Such development will, of course, have to take into consideration the employment opportunities.

There is a parallel need for centres for technician training in both food processing and nutrition. The recently published Unesco Report (Aylward, 1971) reviews food and nutrition education and training within the formal education system in low-income countries. Much could be achieved through the network of sub-university institutions (schools of agriculture, technical institutes, teacher training centres) which already exist in many low-income countries.

The Unesco Report draws attention to the need to link together food science and nutrition programmes at both university and sub-university levels; this indeed has been done at the University of Ghana where the department is styled *Nutrition and Food Science*. By contrast, the term *nutrition* often in practice has a medical connotation, and in several low-income countries programmes have been proposed which are divorced from agricultural production and food processing problems.

Research and development centres for food and nutrition projects cannot be placed on a permanent basis without trained personnel and it is suggested that FAO, Unesco and other appropriate groups should take action on proposals such as the following:

(i) that a plan be worked out for the establishment of food and nutrition departments or sections in universities and technical or other colleges in different regions with financial support to be sought from UNDP, UNICEF and Foundations;

(ii) that meanwhile efforts be made for a large increase in fellowships to be awarded for training in post-harvest problems and nutrition;

(iii) that a review be undertaken on the ways and means of introducing information on nutrition in health education and other curricula in teacher training colleges; and

(iv) that WHO's efforts in the education and training of health personnel, particularly public health specialists and nutritionists be extended and given greater support.

9.12. The diffusion of food and nutrition information

The Unesco Report (Aylward, 1971), to which reference has already been made, makes proposals for the introduction of food and nutrition topics in schools and colleges of education and other teacher training centres. The thirty advanced colleges of education established in different low-income countries with the assistance of Unesco and UNDP could be key centres for the implementation of such proposals. There is, however, a great shortage, even in industrialized countries, of teachers with the knowledge and experience and special training programmes would be required in low-income countries, with fellowships for the training abroad of key personnel.

In low-income countries, the populations are still largely rural, and it is clearly desirable that school curricula dealing with food and nutrition should stress the importance of making the most effective use of indigenous agriculture.

Colleges of education as well as university centres can be encouraged to make a greatly increased contribution to food and nutrition adult education and extension activities. In many countries great efforts have been made to promote *agricultural* extension, but programmes are often concerned primarily with agricultural *production*, with a neglect of *utilization*. There is scope for parallel (and integrated) programmes to reach the village community. In such programmes universities and colleges can play a leading role in preparing texts and notes and visual aid material.

In some countries, food and nutrition commissions and other bodies have begun to make use of the mass media—newspapers, the cinema, radio and television—for the diffusion of food and nutrition information. Although television may be uncommon in low income countries, the radio is widely used and cinemas are often widespread. In some areas, travelling demonstration caravans are used—and those who dismiss this idea may be reminded that "travelling schools" using caravans, were used in Europe in the last century, for example to provide instruction in dairying in rural areas in the United Kingdom.

Films, whether for the cinema or television, require rather heavy capital expenditure, but when we consider the acute shortage of personnel for food and nutrition teaching in low-income countries, it would seem that film production might well be an area for investment by aid agencies. The recent experience of the Open University in the United Kingdom has demonstrated the demand for well-produced lectures, combined with demonstrations, on film or cassettes.

9.13. Medical and public health services for mothers and children

The importance of preventative as well as curative public health services has been stressed in many WHO reports and in other surveys of development policy, so we can limit our comments to a few points.

Many countries are faced with two related problems:

(i) that a high proportion of their health budgets is absorbed in the maintenance of modern hospitals associated with university medical school, often situated in the capital or other large cities; and

(ii) a large proportion of the medically qualified men who are trained prefer to work in larger towns as distinct from rural areas.

In some low-income countries the new medical schools (functioning on the pattern of those in industrialized countries) have achieved considerable prestige and efforts are now being made to re-examine the pattern with a view to creating on a regional basis training centres for para-professional personnel.

Community Health Centres in different forms and under different names (e.g., Mother and Child Centres) have been established in some countries with para-medical personnel able to give practical instruction on the care and feeding of children.

Many physicians believe that protein deficiencies are more common among the age group 1–4 years than in the 0–1 group because children in the latter group have in the past been generally breast fed. Much concern has been expressed over the fact that breast feeding appears to be declining in many countries which are following the patterns of highly industrialized countries. In the latter, some of the undesirable effects of the trend from breast feeding have been largely offset by the almost universal use of manufactured baby foods.

Several companies, mainly of a multinational nature, manufacture these foods and promote their use in low-income countries. However, there is much evidence to suggest that such promotion has had some unexpected and undesirable side effects. It has served to convince mothers that breast feeding is old-fashioned and undesirable. Many mothers have begun to use infant foods, but because of the lack of guidance from doctors or nurses and because of the cost, have supplied their infants with minute quantities, supplementing the diet with protein-poor gruels or even sugar water, with serious protein malnutrition as a consequence. These problems have been discussed at several meetings between nutritionists and representatives of multinational companies active in this field. The meetings earlier sponsored by FAO and WHO are now continued under the auspicies of the Protein Advisory Group (see, for example, the Group's Statement No. 23 on the rational promotion of infant foods).

It must be accepted that for many years to come low purchasing power will prevent the widespread use of branded infant formulas in low-income countries. The development of protein-rich foods manufactured locally and referred to earlier may assist but even these will be beyond the purchasing power of many mothers and beyond the reach of many more, especially in rural areas. There is need, therefore, for the widespread distribution of information on home prepared weaning foods. In this connection, the manual prepared by Cameron and Hofvander (1972) on behalf of the Protein Advisory Group and published with the support of WHO is likely to be very useful.

In recent years it has been demonstrated that problems arise in some countries because individuals or groups cannot tolerate milk; as a result of lactase deficiency the consumption of milk or its products can produce gastro-intestinal upsets. This clearly raises questions as to how far milk can be universally recommended in foods for infants and children.

The Protein Advisory Group Statement No. 17 reviews this problem and concludes that in areas where lactase deficiency is common, the responsible authorities must advise the individuals concerned to use milk substitutes, but that no general action should be taken to reduce the use of milk which has proved so valuable a food for children.

9.14. Nutrition and family size

The relationships between population growth and food supplies has been discussed in many publications; in any one country or region, and in the world as a whole, the levels of food production have to be considered not only in terms of immediate needs but also in terms of increasing (and in some areas) rapidly increasing populations.

There are analogies between the position of developing countries now and the various industrialized countries in the last century, when (as shown in Table 2) high death rates among children were common. In this period large families were also common throughout different economic groups.

National mortality figures are often considered in general *statistical* terms, but it is important to realize the effects on the typical *family* and small community. In industrialized societies, it was assumed in the last century that a high proportion of children born would not survive to maturity; now it can be assumed that most children can reach adult life.

For this reason many who are concerned with population studies and family planning programmes in low-income countries believe that the chances of population stabilization will depend in part on changes—through better nutrition as well as other public health measures—leading to a greater chance of the survival of children within a family. Thus, efforts to decrease illness and deaths from protein-calorie malnutrition and other nutritional deficiencies, must be considered within a wide sociological context of (to use the FAO phrase) better family living. This has led to proposals that nutrition education programmes can advantageously be combined with family planning.

A characteristic feature of many low-income countries is a tradition of long lactation periods and although there is not complete agreement in medical circles, it would appear that through long lactation the probability of conception may be reduced. It has been suggested by the Protein Advisory Group that WHO study this question further.

9.15. Supplementary feeding programmes

For many years to come the nutritional status, especially of children and pregnant and lactating mothers is likely to remain unsatisfactory in many low-income countries. Therefore, attention has to be given to programmes for supplementary food supplies to these groups. Best known in this respect are school lunch programmes but mothers and small children may be reached through community health or similar centres.

These programmes are well known from periods of disaster, but may be needed on a long term basis in many low-income countries. They have been criticized because the free food thus distributed may discourage local food production and also because such programmes must be carefully planned on a long term basis. The Protein Advisory Group is establishing a working group to study how such programmes can best be implemented and, when possible, combined with some component of nutrition education. Rough estimates suggest that the supplementary feeding of school children may cost the equivalent of US $10–15 per year per child. US $30 per person may be required to reach pre-school children and mothers. Because of cost considerations most low-income countries have to limit distribution to those among the vulnerable groups who are most easily reached.

10. The Contribution of Industrialized Countries: Mobilization of Scientific and Technical Resources

10.1 Introduction

One of the key questions raised in the ACAST Report on the impending protein crisis (1968) and taken up in subsequent discussions is "how far can more effective action be taken to mobilize the resources of industrialized countries to deal with the protein problem?" The question can be put in another way—"how far are the present bottlenecks or barriers to improvement caused by a failure to mobilize resources and to transfer information, ideas and sound practices?"

The pattern of contacts between industrialized and developing countries is outlined in Table 11 which shows some of the channels through which can flow scientific and technical information and/or technical economic aid.

The role of the UN System and bi-lateral aid will be considered in the next chapter. The remarks which follow cover a few selected aspects of international contacts which are potentially of importance in respect to nutrition problems.

10.2. Universities and related institutions

The term university is here used to cover all institutions of higher or tertiary education irrespective of their name or official status; it is used therefore for technological and agricultural centres which in many industrialized countries are administrated separately from the older general universities.

The contribution of universities to food and nutrition problems can be considered under three headings:

(a) as training centres for scientific and technical personnel from developing countries and as centres for conferences and seminars;

(b) as centres for active research and development work including contract work on development problems;

TABLE 11. SCIENTIFIC AND TECHNICAL INTER-CONNECTIONS

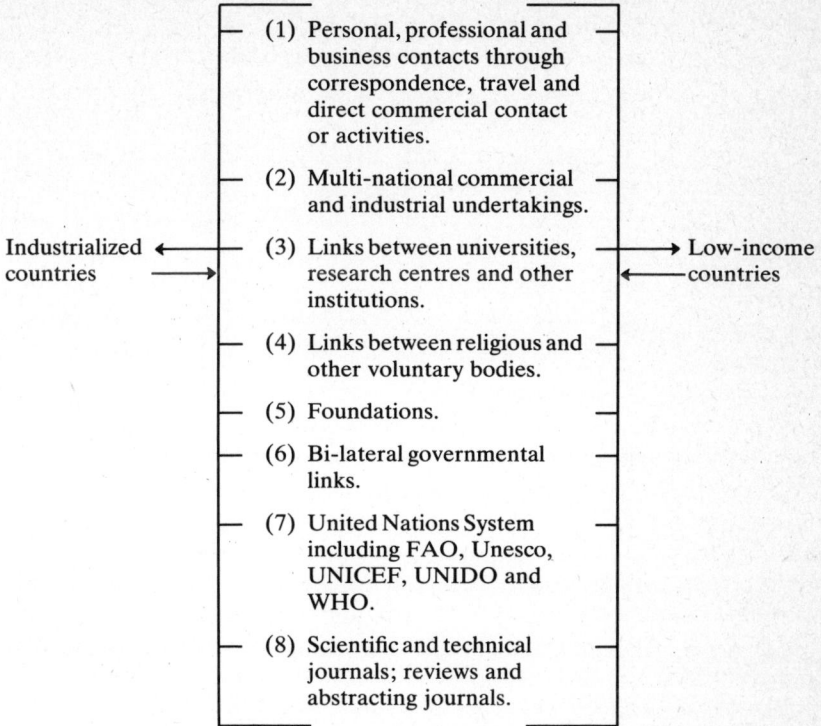

Industrialized countries ⟷

(1) Personal, professional and business contacts through correspondence, travel and direct commercial contact or activities.

(2) Multi-national commercial and industrial undertakings.

(3) Links between universities, research centres and other institutions.

(4) Links between religious and other voluntary bodies.

(5) Foundations.

(6) Bi-lateral governmental links.

(7) United Nations System including FAO, Unesco, UNICEF, UNIDO and WHO.

(8) Scientific and technical journals; reviews and abstracting journals.

Low-income countries

(c) as sources of consultants and specialists to assist in United Nations and bi-lateral development programmes.

There is evidence from individual countries, UN agencies and from the Secretariat of the Protein Advisory Group that there is increased interest in the protein problem in many universities and that this interest has been stimulated by the ACAST Report and by the 1968 Report of the Secretary General, and by subsequent discussions and activities inside and outside the United Nations and its agencies.

Link Schemes

Unesco (1969) has published a report which surveys the *links* that have been forged between universities and other centres in industrialized countries and corresponding centres in developing countries. Although the authors recognize that the lists are incomplete, the extent of the network will surprise and stimulate many readers.

The report points out many advantages of these *link schemes*—in particular the direct involvement of groups, as distinct from isolated individuals, on a continuing basis, and the possibility of action in developing countries, with the approval of the local governments, but in large measure outside the civil service framework.

Some countries, notably the United States, have channelled important sections of technical assistance through link programmes and some UN agencies have also applied the principle of sub-contracting to universities and research centres. In the view of the authors, link schemes can play an important role in the provision of adequate and realistic training programmes for professional personnel in low-income countries and can make research programmes in the industrialized countries on development problems more realistic.

Training Programmes

Over the past two decades tens of thousands of students from low-income countries have travelled for education and training to the universities and technical institutions of Australasia, Europe, North America and the Soviet Union. There is nothing new in this migration, but in recent years it has been on a scale unknown in history, and has been greatly facilitated by grants and training fellowships provided by the UN System, bi-lateral aid agencies and by foundations. The governments of low-income countries are now, to a great extent providing fellowships and travel grants for key personnel selected for overseas training.

Whereas at one time the majority of student migrants went abroad for undergraduate courses, an increasing proportion now travel after taking their first degree in a university in their own country or region. There are many debates on training problems, for example on the importance of postgraduate training through "taught" courses rather than an emphasis on research, and concern has been expressed because of the reluctance of some fellows to return home. Recent experience suggests that this point has sometimes been exaggerated. The fellowship training programmes must be regarded both on a long-term and on a short-term basis as one of the central contributions of the industrialized world to the development of low-income countries.

In food and nutrition training programmes, two problems have arisen in the past:

(i) the relatively small number of institutions outside the United States which have been able to offer specialized training (as distinct from general research) facilities in food science and technology and in nutrition; and

(ii) the relatively small number of fellowships available in food and nutrition compared to many other more traditional fields, such as medicine, agriculture, physical science and engineering.

On a long term basis, institutions must be built up in low-income countries, but for many years to come training will be required in industrialized countries. There are now postgraduate training centres in Australasia, Canada, Europe and the Soviet Union which supplement those in the United States but there is urgent need for an increase in the numbers of fellowships for food and nutrition work.

Research Projects

Many universities in industrialized countries have been engaged in research projects which are directly or indirectly of benefit to low-income countries. Much basic and applied research on food and nutrition is carried out in the universities, but it appears that in comparatively few cases have joint projects been possible with centres in low-income countries. The difficulties arise not from lack of goodwill, but because of administrative and financial reasons.

Over the past three years various UN agencies have been reviewing their policies in respect of universities and scientific institutions. Thus the Director General of FAO has invited a consultant to survey the ways and means of extending FAO's contacts in this field; there is general agreement that external connections with scientific centres must be strengthened with the double objective of stimulating centres in industrial countries to take a greater interest in problems of development and to ensure that FAO personnel, both at headquarters and in the field, have adequate access to scientific and technical information. Action is being taken in different ways; one division of FAO lists major centres of research in the field of animal production with a view to ensuring that the staff of the Division have personal contacts in these centres; another division has prepared a comprehensive, although preliminary, list of training centres and organizations, related to food processing; the Food Policy and Nutrition division has lists of centres working in food and nutrition research and more specifically on protein problems.

The International Atomic Energy Agency, IAEA, has made a special feature of contacts with external institutions and the Joint FAO/IAEA Division which is concerned with the applications of new scientific techniques to food and agriculture problems has devised administrative procedures to catalyse connections between institutions in industrialized and low-income countries. Some of these programmes (e.g. in respect of plant breeding) involve the provision of relatively small grants to stimulate research in universities with procedures for periodic reporting at meetings where groups of research workers on related problems are brought together. It appears that the Agency, by such quite modest means, has succeeded in stimulating work and international cooperation in its field in a very useful manner.

It is hoped that the Consultative Group (mentioned earlier) on Agricultural Research established by FAO, IBRD and various bi-lateral aid agencies and the Ford and the Rockefeller Foundations which allocates very substantial research funds may consider supporting research in the post-harvest field.

At its 20th Session in 1972 the Protein Advisory Group in its Statement No. 12, outlined and assigned priorities to various subjects on which further research is indicated.

Consultancy and Advisory Work

All the United Nations' agencies, as well as national technical assistance organizations, make extensive use of the university personnel as consultants and field workers. In general, universities have been generous in liberating staff for assignments. Difficulties are arising because of increasing demands from overseas and the increasing pressure on universities in terms of "home" student numbers and finance. There are further problems because of the declining numbers (in some European countries at least) of persons with long periods of residence and experience in tropical and other developing countries.

"Link" schemes are of great potential importance in providing experience for staff of different age groups and in promoting continuity in overseas service, but so far as can be ascertained, there are comparatively few link schemes in relation to food and nutrition science and comparatively few "supernumerary" posts endowed by foundations or aid agencies.

The authors strongly recommend that much more use be made of these devices, which are especially suited for bi-lateral aid work. They are very efficient means of ensuring that newly founded institutes in the emerging nations have access to specialists in many disciplines and they give the research efforts in the industrialized societies an invaluable means of continuous field testing with suitable guidance and appropriate feed-back for further work.

Both FAO and WHO, together with UNICEF, have relied extensively on university connections. In respect to nutrition—a few examples may be quoted. Since 1948 FAO and WHO have organized meetings in Geneva or Rome at two or three yearly intervals of a *Joint Expert Committee on Nutrition*. This has provided the two agencies with an opportunity of bringing together a group of specialists from different countries chosen as individuals because of their experience in different fields. The reports of these meetings (which are not as well known as they may merit) provide a history and commentary on nutrition problems since 1948 and embody many suggestions for dealing also with protein nutrition. The Protein Advisory Group, which in a sense arose from these joint meetings, has also depended in large measure on the specialized knowledge of its members recruited as individuals, and many from universities. A similar pattern is seen in many other FAO, Unesco, UNIDO, UNICEF and WHO Committees (e.g. the FAO/WHO Expert Committee on Protein Requirements).

Proposals for Action

It is suggested that FAO, WHO, UNICEF and UNIDO, in conjunction with other technical assistance groups, and possibly through the Protein Advisory Group, should re-examine the university contribution to food and nutrition problems on lines such as the following:

(a) to prepare and publish lists of teaching centres in different countries which provide courses in food and nutrition science;

(b) to determine what assistance is required by the existing centres, or by new centres proposed, in low-income countries and what further assistance can be offered by institutions in industrialized countries;

(c) to encourage further personal contacts between the staff of agencies and institutions;

(d) to determine what steps might be taken to stimulate the establishment of more link schemes;

(e) to review financial and administrative aspects of the above.

In conjunction with (e), two points may be noted as "bottlenecks". In many industrialized countries, even the wealthiest universities and associated institutions are working on restricted budgets with severe problems arising from inflation; machinery must be devised (through national or international action) to provide the extra funds (sometimes relatively small in amount) to stimulate training and research programmes concerned with food and nutrition. The Joint

FAO/IAEA Division's policy has already been noted and may be more generally applicable. National and international foundations may be able to render an important service. Thus one foundation has recently provided a food centre in the United Kingdom with a grant of £40,000 (over a five year period) to provide two extra senior members for the lecturing staff who will be responsible for food courses designed for students from low-income countries. Such grants for training as distinct from research are rare, but extremely useful.

The second bottleneck concerns administrative procedures adopted in development programmes. Some simplification and greater flexibility of procedures might stimulate more university or research centres to cooperate in projects. To a certain extent it appears as if new types of machinery are needed in both bi-lateral and international organization. There are cases where centres of international repute have offered to make brains and manpower available in such link schemes on the assumption that close contacts with a centre in a low-income country could constitute an inspiration for a staff otherwise engaged in rather sophisticated work of a very specialized nature. Yet, no action was possible because adequate machinery did not exist. There are signs, however, that this is being rectified and some promising link schemes have recently been established.

10.3. Technical colleges and other non-university teaching centres

Agricultural, technical, teacher training, and other colleges outside the university system in the industrialized world have played a role, parallel to that of the universities, in providing training facilities, and this service will no doubt be needed for some years to come. There is, however, some measure of agreement that the training of craftsmen and technicians can best be carried out in the low-income country itself and that the main contribution from technical colleges in industrialized countries will be the provision of field staff to assist new institutions. A strong case can be made for link schemes in this field.

As already noted, there is ample scope in most low-income countries for the initiation or extension of technical training in respect to food processing and it is important that this should go on parallel to developments at university level.

10.4. Research institutes

Many research centres in industrialized countries have worked parallel to, and in conjunction with, universities in providing consultative and field staff for development projects. The Unesco publication on "link" schemes, referred to previously, covers research centres as well as universities.

The financial and administrative barriers to the extension of activities in respect to food and nutrition problems are very similar to those in universities. There is need for action designed to mobilize the resources of centres which are concerned with food and nutrition science, with food processing, and with technical information services and "trouble-shooting".

The Protein Advisory Group made a preliminary study of conditions pertaining to research centres in low-income countries related to protein foods and protein nutrition at its meeting in 1972.

10.5. Industry

Over the past few years, different agencies, notably FAO, UNICEF and UNIDO, have made special efforts to interest industrial concerns in the food and nutrition problems of low-income countries. Reports of the FAO/Industry Cooperative Programme indicate that progress has been made, as do reports of various conferences in which speakers from industry have contributed accounts of their activities. Many voluntary scientific and technical bodies in different countries have a wide cross section of membership ranging from universities through research institutes to industry; meetings (such as one organized in 1967 by the American Association of Cereal Chemists on cereal supplementation, and some of the Easter School meetings at universities in the United Kingdom) are of importance in producing cross-fertilization of ideas and also changes in attitudes.

Industry can contribute to the protein problem in at least three ways:

(a) by undertaking research and development work in this field in industrialized countries;
(b) by assisting in the establishing of processing and distribution units in developing countries; and
(c) by making personnel available to the United Nations System and bi-lateral technical development agencies.

In respect to (a) it appears that many of the major food enterprises, and especially those which are multi-national (in the sense that they operate in several different countries) are working actively on protein foods and on animal feeds. In respect to (c) FAO, UNICEF and UNIDO have endeavoured to recruit specialists with industrial experience either on temporary secondment or for long term appointments. Some success has been achieved but there is an obvious need for more men with a suitable experience and outlook to become available.

The main difficulty is in respect to (b). Some food firms are cooperating actively in protein projects in South America and elsewhere, but other firms have been unwilling to take the financial risks, especially as several failures have become known. It seems unlikely that there can be any rapid increase in investment by industry in protein projects until more and successful pilot schemes are in operation in developing countries and until the attitudes of different governments are clarified. Government support to the early stages of industrial projects would be helpful. It has frequently been suggested that a government should accept responsibility for the pilot stage of a project, to turn it over to industry when successful but in the past few such schemes have worked. Governments often do not have the proper personnel and procedures for handling the most critical part of a project, i.e. the exploratory, pilot plant, and early commercial operations, and the transfer of a project from government to industry has proved to be difficult.

As mentioned above, it is difficult for industry to release personnel for a sufficient length of time. It would be beneficial if international and bi-lateral agencies and aid receiving countries would review their procedures in this respect. In the past they have for technical assistance relied very much on hiring individuals, who work under the guidance of the aid agency and/or the host country.

This system has some important disadvantages:

(a) The specialist works for a limited period, often much shorter than the life-time of the project. This causes a serious lack of continuity.

(b) The agency or the country, not the individual, is responsible for the project, but this responsibility is often difficult to define and does not always involve real commitment and involvement by those who are responsible. Moreover, they are often geographically far from the project and overburdened with work.

(c) The project is staffed by a group of individuals brought together for different lengths of time, with different views, backgrounds and approaches. It is very difficult for them to form a team.

(d) Such teams are to a large extent composed of persons on leave from universities or government posts since few industrialists can accept such long time, i.e. often one year or more, yet temporary appointments. This often leads to a skewed composition of technical assistance teams, too few team members having industrial or commercial experience.

Aid agencies might do well to consider inviting industrial organizations to take responsibility and accountability for a whole project, to man it with their own personnel and to provide the necessary base support from their home office. In this way, an already existing organization would be used for executing a task; the reputation of the organization would suffer or be enhanced according to failure or success of the project.

10.6. International scientific and technical bodies

The two main international scientific bodies concerned directly with food and nutrition are the International Union of Nutritional Sciences, IUNS, and the International Union for Food Science and Technology, IUFoST. The IUNS has many connections with the Protein Advisory Group and the UN agencies; it has official relations with WHO, and has submitted a statement supporting the efforts by ACAST and other bodies to promote action on the protein problem. The activities and publications of the IUNS are of special importance because this union links together all the main national voluntary scientific bodies concerned with nutrition, including those in low-income countries. The programme of each of the trienniel congresses over the past decade (including Prague, September 1969 and Mexico, DF, 1972) have included sessions devoted to low-income countries with special emphasis on protein-calorie malnutrition.

In 1970 the International Union of Food Science and Technology (IUFoST) came into existence, at an international congress held in Washington, DC, following earlier congresses in London (1963) and Warsaw (1967). At the Washington meetings there was a strong emphasis on nutritional aspects of food science and various symposia dealt with problems of importance to low-income countries. This was true also of the IUFoST Congress in Madrid (1974).

IUFoST has strong connections in most industrialized countries in both academic and industrial circles; several of its national constituent bodies, as well as individual members of these in industrialized countries, are anxious to extend connections with low-income countries but no appropriate means has yet been found as to how this can be done on a more extensive scale.

Proposals have been worked out for joint action between the IUNS and IUFoST and it is suggested that the Protein Advisory Group and the UN agencies should take steps to encourage further cooperation with both unions in respect to food and nutrition problems. Both were represented at the May 1971 meeting convened by the Secretary General of the UN of the panel of experts which was given a mandate to work out a strategy in respect to the protein problem.

There are various other international unions or equivalent bodies concerned with different aspects of crop and animal production and utilization. The Protein Advisory Group, in conjunction with the United Nations agencies, could make available consolidated lists of such organizations and could take steps to ensure a two-way exchange of ideas and information regarding nutritional problems. One group that deserves special mention is the International Biological Programme (IBP) sponsored by the International Council of Scientific Unions (ICSU). Various sections of the IBP have sponsored projects directly concerned with food and nutrition; although some activities are coming to an end, others may well continue.

Unesco and other agencies are cooperating with IBP and also with a number of bodies concerned with what can broadly be described as applied microbiology and biochemical engineering. These bodies include the International Cell Research Organization (ICRO) and the International Organization for Bio-technology and Bioengineering.

While much enthusiasm exists, we muct accept that there are upper limits to what such bodies can do. Their secretariats cannot undertake any assistance assignments and the members of the various organizations are mostly very busy individuals with very limited, if any, time to take on extra work no matter how urgent. Nevertheless, the organizations can serve as vehicles for the transfer of information, especially through conferences and publications.

10.7. Conferences

Over the past few years increased interest in food and nutrition questions has been reflected in conferences sponsored by both national and international bodies and held in both industrialized and low-income countries. Some of these have dealt with general problems of protein production and utilization and with new protein products; others were concerned with new protein sources such as production from unicellular organisms (SCP) or with special topics

such as amino-acid supplementation of cereals, calorie-protein requirements, proteins in relation to mental development, and protein
determination. The proceedings of several of these conferences have
been published and form useful additions to the literature on health,
scientific, technical and economic aspects of protein nutrition and
protein foods. Some of these printed proceedings are listed in the
bibliography of this volume.

10.8. Publications

The question of publications is all-important both in stimulating
interest in food and nutrition and in detailing methods for action.
Within FAO and other organizations (including the Protein Advisory
Group) valuable information, often in the form of reports from
consultants and specialists in field posts, has been collected but has
been only sparsely incorporated into the scientific and technical
literature. Much of the documentation has remained in mimeographed form and there have been difficulties in classification and
distribution. FAO is aware of this problem and initiated in 1969 a
documentation service in terms of a comprehensive index to be
followed by monthly supplements listing new papers. The service will
also provide selected bibliographies.

The Food Policy and Nutrition Division of FAO expanded and
publishes on a regular basis its Nutrition Newsletter which is sent free
(in English, French and Spanish editions) to some 5000 individuals
and institutions in most countries of the world. The Newsletter goes
to individuals who are directly involved in problems of protein calorie
malnutrition and in nutrition matters generally and is an important
medium for the dissemination of information. The Nutrition Newsletter supplements the various printed and priced reports which are
published at intervals from the Division.

Several papers related to protein nutrition have been published in
the *WHO Bulletin* and *WHO Chronicle*, and a special issue of *World
Health* devoted to nutrition was issued in 1969. The *PAG Bulletin* has
been expanded and is now published quarterly in English, French and
Spanish, and efforts are being made to achieve a wider distribution of
selected PAG memoranda and reports to interested individuals and
groups.

Information on the protein problem is required at different levels
in different degrees of detail:

  (a) general publications for the non-specialist;
  (b) scientific publication;
  (c) manuals for practical training and operations.

In respect to (a), FAO published on behalf of the Protein Advisory Group in 1970 a booklet *Lives in Peril* giving general information about protein nutrition. Later the Protein Advisory Group commissioned a general study of protein-rich mixtures which has been published in 1972 by the Tropical Products Institute in London, England.

Many general reviews have been issued over the past years by individuals or groups through ordinary publishing channels. Some of these have tended to over-emphasize new developments (e.g. unconventional protein foods) as distinct from agricultural sources. One useful publication, *Foods Resources, Conventional and Novel,* by Pirie, was issued in 1969 in paper-back form.

In respect of (b); publications for the professional scientist have already been mentioned. It is suggested that fuller use be made of the scientific abstracting journals, including *Nutrition Abstracts and Reviews* and *International Abstracts on Food Science and Technology,* to ensure that relevant publications on proteins are listed.

At some point in time, it was hoped that the Protein Advisory Group might be able to act as an information centre on questions relating to protein foods and protein nutrition. Shortage of funds has made it impossible for the Group's Secretariat to act in this capacity; however, through the *PAG Bulletin* and its other activities the Group may be able to advocate the more widespread use of the above mentioned sources of information. Where special subjects are considered of importance to the Group, information searches may be commissioned to some documentation centre and the ensuing study made available to anyone interested.

In respect to (c), much published information is of a general character and lacks *detailed* accounts of processing or other techniques. This is a serious barrier to progress in developing countries where manuals for use at the sub-university or foremans' level would be welcome. A useful series of practical reports on methods of food processing is being issued by the Agricultural Services Division of FAO, and UNIDO has published monographs on topics such as oil-seed processing. Reference to these is found in the bibliography to this volume.

It is suggested that the Protein Advisory Group, in conjunction with the UN agencies, should prepare a bibliography listing publications available on different phases of protein nutrition for different levels of readership and that consideration be given to the preparation of booklets which can fill in gaps, and to the reprinting of such existing publications which may deserve a wider international circulation.

One barrier arises from the very high cost of many of the standard text and reference books; hence the importance at this stage of subsidized publications. Much could be achieved if financial provision could be made to enable publications on different aspects of food and nutrition to be widely distributed at a low cost in low-income countries.

Reference has already been made to the information available in mimeographed reports in the UN agencies. The policy in the different agencies, and often within any one agency, has been uneven. It is suggested that officers of UN agencies and field staff be encouraged or even required to summarize mimeographed reports and, subject to the necessary clearance and editorial procedures, to submit papers for publication in scientific or technical journals and periodicals. An increase in such published work could add to our knowledge and would moreover discourage the repetition of work already carried out, but unpublished; it could also serve to enhance the prestige of the UN agencies in scientific and other circles by providing evidence of projects undertaken and of achievements. It is realized that "clearance" of these publications often involves many officials, both within a host country and the UN System; this is probably the main obstacle to be overcome but the problem merits renewed consideration.

10.9. Systems approach

Especially in ACAST reports it has been suggested that countries, and the UN for the World as a whole, apply a system approach to determine the most efficient means of eliminating protein malnutrition. This proposal was examined by the Protein Advisory Group. In its Statement No. 10 issued in 1970, it expressed the view that the necessary data are yet insufficient to make such an approach meaningful but the Group found it desirable to obtain further data with the aim that sometime in the future a workable model might be developed.

In the view of the authors, it might be interesting and indeed even useful if some academic or similar institutions would actually attempt to develop a world, regional or national model for a systems approach to the protein or rather the protein-calorie nutrition/supply system. Many data and relationships would be available only in fragmentary form but it is likely that exercises of this kind would best disclose those areas where further data are most urgently needed.

FAO is also increasing its interest in such an approach in that its Food Policy and Nutrition Division is developing data for a so-called nutrimetrics approach to nutrition development.

11. The Contribution of the United Nations' Agencies, National Technical Assistance Agencies, International Foundations and Voluntary Bodies

11.1. Introduction

In earlier chapters many references have been made to the technical assistance and development activities of the UN agencies, but it is important to remember that many other groups are also involved.

Some of these, namely educational and research centres and industry have already been discussed. Three others require some comment, namely (i) national technical assistance agencies; (ii) foundations; and (iii) voluntary bodies.

It is impossible to describe here the different facets of the work of the many bodies concerned, so our notes will be limited to a few examples of work already being carried out, or opportunities for further activities, in respect to food and nutrition.

11.2. National technical assistance agencies

Technical assistance programmes from a donor country normally involve direct *government to government* connections and the type of activities therefore depend in very large measure on the type of request that comes from the recipient country. Aid may cover a spectrum ranging from loans or gifts of money through gifts of equipment, to arrangements for the support of field personnel, and facilities for fellowships to provide education and training in the donor countries.

In some donor countries the emphasis is on direct government action with technical assistance personnel directly responsible to the government. In other countries various types of "devolution" have taken place so that part of the aid flows along different channels for example:

(i) through contracts involving industry or educational or research centres.

(ii) through the establishment and/or encouragement of non-governmental or semi-governmental bodies to undertake aid.

(iii) through the establishment by trust-fund or other means) of active cooperation with FAO (or some other UN Agency).

(iv) through cooperation with other nations for aid on a regional basis with multi-national contributions.

As already noted, the contract principle (i) has been extensively employed by the US Government in the encouragement of aid through the universities; the land-grant institutions in particular have taken an active part in agricultural and food projects.

In various countries semi-governmental bodies have been encouraged. Thus the Inter-University Council in the United Kingdom has been the intermediary in many programmes of aid to institutions in Africa, the West Indies and Malaysia leading to the establishment of several, now important, Faculties of Agriculture.

The Canadian-sponsored International Development Research Centre established in 1970 with an international Board of Trustees has an active programme in respect to agriculture and the food industries.

Various countries have worked out plans with FAO for the joint sponsorship of projects. Among the most successful of these has been those supported by the Danish Government in respect to the training of personnel for the dairy industry. Projects have included the establishment of technical training centres (usually embodying a well-equipped milk processing plant) in a low-income country, and training courses held in Denmark or overseas.

The governments of the Netherlands, West Germany, Denmark and other countries have cooperated with FAO in the programme of *associate experts,* to provide a corps of young graduates who can work overseas, initially under supervision, in preparation for careers in technical assistance and other posts.

11.3. Foundations

Several references have been made to the activities of the Ford and Rockefeller Foundations which have made important contributions to agricultural development. A few other foundations have been concerned with specific food and nutrition projects for example the Kellogg Foundation (US) in its support for teaching centres and the

Leverhulme Trust (UK) in its assistance to post-graduate education. The Dag Hammarskjöld Foundation (Sweden) has organized a number of symposia on problems of low income countries including one on *Nutrition as a Priority in African Development*. The Nestle Foundation has an active programme of research into nutrition problems on the Ivory Coast and is supporting food research projects in low-income countries. In conjunction with the Ciba Foundation it arranged an important scientific symposium dealing with aspects of malnutrition in relation to the development of the human brain.

11.4. Voluntary organization

A large number of voluntary charitable bodies in different industrial countries are concerned with overseas aid and have collected and distributed considerable sums of money. Many, although by no means all, of the bodies are religious groups which are in part linked together internationally.

Several of the groups have cooperated actively with UNICEF which, although for convenience is usually listed among UN Agencies, is supported by voluntary donations. The *Freedom from Hunger* campaign sponsored by FAO depended for its success largely on voluntary groups in various countries.

Many of the voluntary organizations were established primarily to deal with *emergency relief* during and after World War II; they still play an important role in emergency, including disaster relief, both through the mobilization of personal aid services, and through food and other supplies.

Over the past few years the voluntary organizations have become increasingly interested in projects designed to be of permanent value in improving local conditions in low-income countries; their programmes have the great potential advantage of providing support for groups (or projects) which may fall outside the area of the bi-lateral (or UN) government-to-government assistance. Although the position varies from one organization to another, there is a belief in some circles that the voluntary bodies have still to define more precisely their role and to work out plans to secure adequate technical advice to support their humanitarian efforts.

No comment on voluntary activities would be complete without a reference to the various programmes to encourage individuals to serve in field posts through organizations such as the *Peace Corps* (US), Voluntary Service Overseas (UK), U-lands frivillige (Denmark) or similar bodies in other countries.

11.5. Cooperation between organizations

Examples have already been given of cooperation between national, official and voluntary bodies and the UN agencies. Many observers believe that there is need for greatly increased cooperation between the officers of organizations at headquarter level, and even more so between field personnel. When we know the seriousness of problems, in regard to food and nutrition, as well as in other fields, it becomes especially important to encourage the interchange of information and experience. Some technical assistance personnel are often unaware of the efforts that have already been made in low-income countries in the subject areas in which they themselves work, and in related subject areas of importance in the establishment of priorities and national policy. There is at present little provision for informing new advisers of earlier work. The recent publication from Uganda providing a bibliography of nearly 1000 references to books and reports in the food and nutrition field reveals the vast amount of information potentially available from older and more recent investigations.

In respect to food and nutrition, more could be achieved if personnel from both official and voluntary bodies made greater efforts to obtain FAO, PAG and other UN documentation on a subject basis, and also on a country or regional basis. Conversely the headquarters, regional and country representation of UN agencies have an important role in offering services to those working outside the UN system. In any one country the office of the Resident Representatives of the UN Development Programme can become a key centre for the exchange of information and experiences.

11.6. Attitudes in low-income countries

Answers to the questionnaire on the protein problem sent by the UN Secretary-General to UN members indicate that in many low-income countries there is now a keen interest in nutrition problems and a desire to take action both to raise general nutritional standards and to increase the production and consumption of protein. Over the past few years there appears to have been significant changes in thinking and in most countries it is recognized that nutritional programmes are indicated especially in relation to child health and that efforts must be made, mainly through agriculture, to increase the supplies of food crops.

Few countries, however, have accepted fully the concept of a national food and nutrition policy. It is still relatively uncommon to have a senior Minister responsible for *food* (as distinct from agriculture and from public health); few low-income countries have senior civil servants (administrative, scientific or technical) whose *primary* responsibility is to look at the question of food supplies, and their nutritional value. From many points of view the picture is similar to that in Europe before World War II when questions of food supplies were largely left alone.

Thus in spite of the interest in protein and associated nutritional questions much remains before food and nutrition policy is regarded as an essential aspect of national policy. This is reflected also in the fact that although there are many food and nutrition projects in the medical and agricultural fields; there are relatively few centres of education and training, research and development concerned with what has been described in this booklet as the *post-harvest field*.

11.7. The UN system—recent developments

The UN agencies, including FAO and WHO and associated bodies such as UNICEF and UNIDO have been able to exercise an important influence in stimulating interest among increasing numbers of public health officers, and in matters of agricultural production; for reasons given in earlier sections of this review they have been less successful in respect to programmes centred around food science and food processing and the establishment of food industries.

The World Bank, i.e. the International Bank for Reconstruction and Development (IBRD), took a major step when its president, Mr Robert McNamara, in 1971 declared that in addition to population projects, the Bank would give increased support to nutrition problems. In this, the Bank followed a policy of increased attention to socially oriented problems, i.e. the quality of life, as contrasted with specific economic development, i.e. efforts to increase gross domestic products (GDP).

As a consequence the Bank changed and enlarged its Population Division to a *Population and Nutrition Division* and engaged staff with specific expertise in this field. However, so far the Bank has found it difficult to implement this policy because the Bank must insist on projects being "bankable", i.e. having some component of recovering the investment, even over very long periods and at very low interest rates. Obviously, this is difficult in nutrition projects where, for instance, a general improvement of child health may be achieved with little or no identifiable economic return. In fact, such improvement may be an economic strain on the country's resources, because of better child survival creating a need for more housing and more jobs.

11.8. The UN contribution

The UN system can make contributions to food and nutrition policy in at least six ways:

   (i) by providing, through the specialized agencies and the Protein Advisory Group, *scientific, technical* and *economic* information, for member governments and international foundations, and for scientific, medical, agricultural and industrial organizations;

  (ii) by acting as a channel of *general* information to assist, in both high-income and low-income countries, in creating public interest and a desire for action;

 (iii) by assisting in the formulation of policies;

  (iv) by promoting cooperation between the UN technical agencies, national technical assistance agencies, international foundations and voluntary bodies with a view to ensuring that food and nutrition is accorded a higher priority in technical aid programmes. It is important to recognize that the UN Secretariat, its agencies and associated bodies have developed an intimate knowledge of conditions and development possibilities in low-income countries. Full use must be made of this unique expertise in development efforts;

   (v) by securing funds, directly and indirectly, for programmes concerned with protein—and general food and nutritional programmes.

         In this, the United Nations, its agencies and related bodies might consider reorganizing their secretariat and amending staffing policies to allow for greater involvement in the development of food storage, processing and preservation projects;

  (vi) acting on the proposal made by the Panel of Experts called by the Secretary General of the United Nations in 1971 to consider protein problems confronting developing countries in arranging that members of the panel visit some countries concerned to discuss with governments the need for adopting national nutrition policies, and the means of making such policies more effective.

The replies to the questionnaire of the UN Secretary-General, the reports prepared by FAO, WHO, UNICEF and the Protein Advisory

Group, and the publications of the UN itself show that there is no shortage of *ideas*; the barriers lie in the shortage of trained men and women especially in the low-income countries, and in finance, and possibly in a will to accord nutrition projects high priority in development plans.

11.9. The Protein Advisory Group

The three UN Agencies FAO, WHO, UNICEF which are primarily concerned with protein matters established joint support to the Protein Advisory Group in 1960 to advise on limited aspects of the protein problem. The Group itself was established in 1955, by WHO to advise that organization. Over the past years the Group has widened its scope and it is now sponsored by additional sectors of the UN System including IBRD and the UN Secretariat. It was renamed the Protein Advisory Group of the UN System in 1971. In its new form the Protein Advisory Group—in association with the sponsoring agencies—can expand and strengthen its information role.

Recommendations and resolutions both from the United Nations Advisory Committee on the Application of Science and Technology to Development (ACAST), and the United Nations General Assembly have suggested that the Secretariat of the Protein Advisory Group should serve as a centre for information in the field of protein nutrition or even in nutrition generally as it relates to low-income countries. However, the funds allocated to the Group's functions and those of its Secretariat will only allow for the Group to have one meeting per year, with one additional meeting of its steering committee per year and for its Secretariat to service these meetings, publishing the *PAG Bulletin* with reasonable frequency, and servicing two or three special working groups or technical meetings (such as those on legumes or infant foods) a year. Even with these limitations the Group can serve as a highly useful policy adviser for governments, bi-lateral agencies, international organizations, foundations and scientific bodies. In 1973, the Group issued its Statement No. 25 in which it outlines critical areas in world food supply and nutrition. This statement, which is reproduced as Appendix 2, is designed to serve as such a guide for food and nutrition policy.

11.10. Bi-lateral agencies

Much assistance to low-income countries is channelled through national bi-lateral agencies. These generally follow a rather strict policy of trying to respond to requests made by the low-income countries without any attempt to influence the priorities which these countries assign to various subjects and often without any informed evaluation of a project's chances of success. It is suggested by the authors that bi-lateral agencies:

(i) attempt to make requesting countries more aware of the need for attention to nutrition problems as outlined and formulated by the United Nations General Assembly, FAO conferences, World Health Assemblies, the United Nations Advisory Committee on the Application of Science and Technology to Development and by the Protein Advisory Group of the United Nations System, and

(ii) involve the experience available in industry, universities, government research and development establishment and the international organizations to provide for full use of existing experience and knowledge in formulating development programmes and projects.

The important question that remains is finance, and in particular financial support guaranteed for an extended, e.g. five-year period for some of the projects outlined in this book. The problem of financing protein projects have been the subject of discussions in the ACAST (1968), the United Nations General Assembly and the Secretary-General's Panel on the Protein Problem Confronting Developing Countries (1971). Out of these comes the recommendation that within the UN system, presumably under the UNDP, a special fund should be set up for financing protein related projects. This fund would be parallel to the UN Population Fund. However, it appears as if UN member countries at this time are not prepared to accept this proposal; most feel that, within the general framework of the United Nations technical assistance machinery, countries should be free to select their own priorities.

11.11. Some priorities

When nutrition projects are considered by governments, the authors would give priority to:

(i) the initiation and strengthening of centres in low-income countries for education and training and for development work in the post-harvest utilization of agricultural crops, with a very considerable increase in funds for overseas training and contacts;

(ii) the establishment of prototype small-scale factories in selected low-income countries for the production of low-cost protein foods, especially those designed for infants and young children;

(iii) efforts to improve family eating patterns and home preparation of adequate weaning foods;

(iv) clinical studies of the nutritional status in low-income countries.

(i) and (ii) can be integrated in that a pilot or small-scale plant can be used for training purposes, although training programmes must, of course, be placed on a wider basis to supply an adequate background in food and nutrition science.

11.12. Training programmes

Parallel to the above, it is suggested that renewed efforts be made to assist low-income countries in their internal administrative and technical efforts to form effective national food and nutrition councils, or units in appropriate Ministries. Governments, in conjunction with UN Agencies, could consider projects such as the following:

(i) plans for the training of *at least one* person for each of the key ministries concerned with nutrition (normally these would be health, agriculture and food, and education) to be trained to act as food and nutrition officers *within* the ministry concerned;

(ii) the recruitment by FAO of a task force of specialists to be available over the next five years to assist developing countries wishing to establish food and nutrition councils or similar organs of government with the understanding that where necessary the FAO recruited staff could provide the secretariat (e.g. for a three-year period) for such organs. Because of the relative shortage in industrialized countries of individuals with the right experience it would be necessary to recruit persons from different disciplines (e.g. nutrition, food science, economics) and to arrange for a period of training;

(iii) training programmes for nutritionists, food scientists and economists from developing countries in the techniques required for the operation of food and nutrition councils or similar bodies and in the techniques of food planning. It would be necessary to make provision for economists to be taught the basic principles of nutrition, both in respect of

protein and other problems, and for those trained in nutrition and food science to be instructed in the principles of economics and planning techniques.

11.13. Conclusions

Problems related to protein nutrition have been many; at times opinions have differed to such an extent that governments and individuals have tended to devote their energies to less controversial and more tangible development subjects. Therefore, a few important facts need to be repeated.

Especially in low-income countries, a problem of protein deficiency exists affecting mainly pregnant and nursing mothers, infants and pre-school children. For those most seriously affected, health and mental development may be affected, and a number of small children may die due to its effects.

The solution lies primarily in improving the distribution of protein foods among different social and geographical groups and even within families.

Better food habits and patterns, often by achieving better utilization of existing supplies, is one of the main requisites for alleviating the situation.

In the long run, increased food *production* is also necessary for the prevention of both under-nutrition and malnutrition. However, parallel to efforts for the improvement of primary production, increased emphasis must be given to improved storage, preservation and processing from the source of food to the ultimate consumers.

In many countries changes in outlook and philosophies will be required to ensure that adequate attention is given to food production and to utilization. Changes in terminology and in administrative practices may also be required. Thus in the university and research sector a change from a Faculty (or College) of Agriculture to *Food* and Agriculture may be a prerequisite for active work in the post-harvest field. At Government level a change from a Ministry of Agriculture to a Ministry of *Food* and Agriculture may be necessary to provide effective support for new initiatives. The title and programme of FAO, the *Food* and Agriculture Organisation of the United Nations, can provide the background for twin, but interlocking, programmes to enable countries to make the fullest use of their indigenous national natural resources to obtain adequate foods for increasing populations.

Appendix 1

The PAG from its inception has dealt with protein-calorie malnutrition and has always considered protein deficiency in relation to the concomitant need for calories and other essential nutrients. The term protein-calorie malnutrition (PCM) includes many different clinical syndromes, all of which are accompanied by retardation of growth and development. The manifestations of PCM vary widely, depending on the nature of the causative factors, the time for which they operate, and the age of the patient. Two severe clinical forms are recognized: nutritional marasmus and kwashiorkor. The former results from deprivation of protein and calories to a similar degree and the latter is due primarily to a protein deficiency relative to energy intake but may be superimposed on any degree of marasmus and is commonly precipitated by infectious episodes. While in some areas PCM could be reduced by increased consumption of cereal-based diets, provided they can meet both protein and calorie needs, foods richer in protein than these would make easier the prevention of such malnutrition and are essential for its treatment. In populations for which starchy roots or tubers make up the basic dietary staple, better sources of protein are essential for both prevention and treatment of the PCM associated with such diets. The more that either cereal- or tuber-based diets are supplemented by legumes, the less the need for introducing other protein-rich foods of animal or plant origin.

The increased cereal production resulting from the Green Revolution that has occurred in some developing countries has not eliminated the concern for ensuring adequate protein in the diets of their populations. This is because the increased production has been almost entirely confined to cereal grains that do not in themselves contain sufficient high-quality protein relative to their bulk and caloric value to meet the optimum needs of young children, particularly those in unfavourable circumstances.

On the contrary, the Green Revolution has accelerated a long-term trend toward a decrease in *per caput* production, as well as an

increase in price, of the legumes that have been the traditional sources of more concentrated protein to supplement predominantly cereal diets. Furthermore, in those areas of the world where the diet is still composed mostly of starchy roots (e.g. cassava, *Manihot utilissima*), tubers (e.g. yams, *Dioscorea, Colocasia, Xanthosoma* spp.) or fruits (e.g. plantain, *Musa sapientium* var. *paradisiaca*), there is often an urgent need to increase protein consumption. The primary purpose of the PAG is to assure that the pre-school child and other vulnerable groups receive a diet adequate in both protein and calories as well as in other essential nutrients.

It is also apparent that with the continuing rapid increase in world population it will be far easier to provide the basic staple, whether it is a cereal or starchy root, tuber, or fruit, than it will be to provide the legume, oil-seed, or animal protein needed in addition by major vulnerable segments of the population: infants and young children, pregnant and lactating women, and persons under the stress of infectious or other diseases. For this reason, the PAG continues to emphasize the desirability of genetic improvement in the protein characteristics of cereals and other staple food crops, enrichment of staple diets with good sources of plant or animal protein, research and fiscal policies that will improve legume and oil-seed production for human feeding, improvement of animal protein supplies and, where this is not feasible the development of vegetable protein mixtures that can serve in place of animal protein for infant and child feeding.

The PAG recognizes that a dietary deficiency of calories relative to protein is wasteful of protein. It is also clear that provision of extra calories from starchy roots and tubers or from sugar and fat without ensuring adequate protein is of limited value.

Analysis of protein needs relative to calories is complicated by the fact that the safe minimum allowances for dietary intake of protein and calories as proposed by FAO/WHO experts are not satisfactory criteria for determining the relative adequacy of protein and calories for vulnerable groups in developing countries. The allowances are for the needs of healthy individuals and underestimate requirements for persons exposed to chronic or recurrent acute infections. The metabolic losses of tissue protein during acute infections result in significantly increased protein needs during convalescence. Absorption of protein may also be reduced by the effects of recurrent enteric infection on the gastrointestinal mucosa and by the presence of intestinal parasites.

Of critical importance is the fact that *per caput* estimates of protein needs do not take into account the effects of maldistribution within

social and economic groups and among family members. If people can afford it and supplies permit, they eat far more protein than they appear to require according to current estimates for healthy individuals. Food available within a family may be consumed disproportionately by adults or working males and often not enough of the foods richer in protein than the basic staple is allotted to young children or other vulnerable family members. For these reasons, *per caput* food and nutrient availability figures can be quite misleading. Direct examination of feeding practices and health conditions among individuals in the vulnerable groups is more informative, but must be interpreted in the light of the added requirement for protein imposed by the factors mentioned.

The PAG recognizes and emphasizes that the protein problem cannot be solved from the supply side alone. It requires an increase in the demand for appropriate protein foods for the feeding of vulnerable groups whether the limiting factor is lack of purchasing power or inadequate knowledge. Environmental, educational and public health measures to reduce the burden of infection on vulnerable groups are also essential.

Because the protein problem is due to inadequate distribution of protein foods to vulnerable groups relative to their needs, it is largely independent of *per caput* protein availability. Moreover, it does not necessarily require solution by the introduction of unfamiliar foods. It could be met by better distribution of food within the family or by increased use of legumes or of animal protein by the groups in need. Nevertheless, processed foods utilizing relatively inexpensive protein of vegetable origin can be very useful for both the prevention and treatment of PCM, especially for urban populations.

The name Protein Advisory Group has caused misunderstanding about the PAG's attention to calories and other nutrients as well as protein. A change to Protein-Calorie Advisory Group has been considered but was rejected because a special effort was needed in programmes of the United Nations system to ensure adequate dietary protein relative to calories. The need for adequate calories has been more generally recognized and major efforts to increase calorie supplies are underway. The PAG also reviews special problems which arise with regard to safety and suitability of new sources of protein, particularly for younger children.

The following questions are among those most frequently asked about the "Protein Problem", and the PAG position is concisely summarized.

1. Is there a protein gap?

If one looks at figures for world and *per caput* availability of protein, the answer is *no*. FAO's Agricultural Commodity Projections for 1970 to 1980, based upon national food balance sheet data submitted to FAO by Member Governments, were calculated according to safe levels of intake recommended by the FAO/WHO Expert Committee Report (1973) on protein requirements for *healthy* men, women, children and infants. These projections show that the *per caput* level of protein supplies available for human consumption exceeds those safe levels by 70%. Further confirmation of the accuracy of the information derived from food balance sheets and clearer definition of what constitutes safe levels of protein intake are needed, but there is no doubt that there is enough dietary protein in the world *if* there were any way it could be distributed according to need. However, there is much evidence that protein foods are not distributed in direct proportion to individual need. The data available indicate that the amounts of both protein and calories actually reaching the pre-school child are seriously inadequate in most of the developing countries. These inadequacies, coupled with recurrent episodes of infectious disease, are the cause of the widespread protein malnutrition seen in the world today.

2. Is there a protein problem?

The answer is *yes*. The continuing high prevalence of protein-calorie malnutrition among children of the developing countries is *prima facie* evidence that suitable foods are not provided to such children, and, in many countries, that cultural practices deny young children sufficient access to protein foods. Suitable foods would, of necessity, provide relatively concentrated sources of energy and would be adequate in protein and other nutrients. Increased cereal production alone will not improve this situation to any significant degree. In this sense, the assurance of a supply and consumption of suitable protein-rich foods for vulnerable groups is a continuing "protein problem".

In some cases the deficiency is equally one of calories and protein, but the protein component of the deficiency is frequently of special concern. This is because foods containing high-quality protein are inequitably distributed between developed and developing regions of the world, between high and low socioeconomic groups within countries, and within households where the vulnerable members

rarely receive a share of the available protein foods commensurate to their needs.

The problem arises from:

(a) low wages and income, and underemployment or unemployment in rural or urban areas, all of which limit the purchase of the relatively costly foods that contain protein of good quality,

(b) difficulties associated with the production of protein-rich foods of animal or plant origin because of ecological and agricultural limitations with the result that they are usually costly and in relatively short supply,

(c) the lack of effective food processing, distribution and marketing systems resulting in loss of food crops, and

(d) lack of knowledge of food values and food preparation for children and specific prejudices against giving some protein foods to young children, especially when they have an infectious illness.

3. Is there a protein problem for adults in developing countries?

Not if the basic staple is wheat or millet, consumed in adequate quantities to meet caloric needs, and if individuals stay healthy. This is also the case, with less margin, for populations eating sorghum, rice or maize at adequate energy levels. However, optimum recuperation from severe infections, especially if repeated or chronic, and from trauma, requires a diet higher in protein value than that supplied by cereal-based diets if they are nearly devoid of animal protein and very limited in legumes and pulses. When starchy roots, tubers, or plantain are the staple, the poor may have insufficient other protein foods in their diet to make up for the small amounts of protein in these staples.

4. Cannot protein-calorie malnutrition be prevented by increasing the quantity of the traditional diet?

In some areas of the world this may be the case, but in most developing countries it is unlikely. For young children, particularly those under three years of age, the traditional diet is frequently so bulky that they have difficulty in eating enough of it to meet fully either calorie or protein needs. It really depends on whether the traditional diet contains enough supplementary animal or plant protein of good quality to meet not only the recommended allowances for healthy children but also to cover the needs of those

suffering from the diarrheal and other infectious diseases that are frequent among young children in developing countries.

Traditional diets may be improved with respect to protein through home preparation of foods such as legumes. In some situations, a processed weaning food mixture containing vegetable protein may be the most practical substitute for the traditional role of animal milks in child feeding. However, this approach is primarily applicable to urban populations and even there the lowest income groups may have difficulty in purchasing sufficient quantities of these foods.

In those areas where fibrous and starchy foods make up much of the diet, it is essential to reduce the bulk by increasing the concentrations of energy and protein weaning foods. This would necessitate attempts to reverse cultural prohibitions that preclude offering sufficient legumes and animal protein foods to weanlings and toddlers. In any area where the staple foods given to young children are very low in protein, protein-rich foods must be added to the diet.

5. Do populations adapt to protein-calorie deficiency and thereby lower their requirements for food?

Not in a true sense. Adults adapt to calorie insufficiency by loss of body weight and reduction of voluntary work; children "adapt" by retarded growth rates, as well as by decreased activity. Such "adaptations" are unacceptable as national policy. The health and productivity of adults may be affected and for children the ultimate result may be impairment of physical and perhaps mental development.

6. Do some ethnic groups have lower requirements than others for protein and for calories?

Not so far as we now know, except that groups differ in requirements insofar as their body weights differ. Inadequate early feeding and frequent infectious episodes during early growth are largely responsible for the smaller body size of some ethnic groups. Recurrent infections in the people of the developing countries tend to increase their needs for protein and other nutrients. Energy requirements will vary with patterns of physical activity and, to some extent, with environmental temperatures. . .

Appendix 2

PAG STATEMENT (No. 25) ON THE GLOBAL MAL-
DISTRIBUTION OF PROTEIN:

A GROWING TREND*

At the 17th Session of PAG, May 1970, the group had an opportunity to comment on the FAO Indicative World Plan (IWP) for Agricultural Development. The comments from which the following extracts are reproduced were prepared for use in discussions at the Second World Food Congress.

". . . (c) According to the IWP the effective demand for proteins, and especially for meat and fish, will not be covered by the supplies offered in the period considered; consequently, as stressed in the IWP, the demand hypothesis based on projections at constant prices is not likely to be realized for this type of product. Unless special measures are taken the demand in relation to available supplies will result in increases in prices. This will result in an increased deficit in consumption by the less-favored population groups. . .

". . . (e) In general, the increase in demand for animal proteins which may be due to an increase in overall income may not improve the nutritional level of the groups which have the most urgent need. On the contrary, their situation may be aggravated.

"(f) For a long time to come there will be a need for programs which will underline the importance of preserving proteins for those who have the highest need for them, inside the family, among various socioeconomic groups and between different ages and classes.

"(g) The production of high-quality proteins, especially dairy products, should be encouraged where feasible in developing countries. In support of these projects, food aid programs will be of value to governments attempting to achieve a harmonious development of their economy with simultaneous improvement in the diet of the population . . ."

---

* PAG Bulletin 1973, Vol. III, No. 3. This statement was prepared following discussions held at the 21st PAG Meeting, 4–8 June 1973, New York. It is based on information presented by Mr. Lester Brown, Overseas Development Council, Washington, DC, USA.

Since then there has been a tremendous increase in the demand for animal feed in the face of continuous adverse circumstances for productivity. These factors have largely aggravated the trend described in the above paragraphs and the international market in 1973 is witnessing a phenomenal increase in price of man's principal food commodities, including wheat, rice and soya beans. These developments have evoked widespread concern for the nutritional status of the economically-handicapped sections of the world population. While historically the global food situation has been discussed largely as a population-food supply problem, we are now witnessing the emergence of rising affluence as a major new claimant on world food resources.

Over four-fifths of the annual increase in world population of an estimated 75 million occurs in poor countries, which are now struggling to find not only food but also opportunities for remunerative and productive employment for their fast-growing populations. In poor countries, which represent the majority of mankind, the *per capita* availability of grain averages about 190 kg per year, most of which is consumed directly to meet minimum energy needs. In contrast, the *per capita* utilization of grain is currently approaching one ton per year in the United States and Canada; of this, only about 70 kg are consumed directly in the form of bread and similar products, the rest being channelled through the plant-animal-man food chain.

The annual *per capita* consumption of beef has risen in the United States from 25 kg in 1940 to 52 kg in 1972. The same trend is seen in many countries in Western and Eastern Europe, the Soviet Union and Japan. As a result, an increasing proportion of the world's grain and oil-seed production is utilized for feeding animals to meet the demand for animal products in affluent nations.

This power of affluence to attract and consume much of the world's food and feed grains, together with a stagnation in the world fish catch since 1969, the recent disappearance of the anchoveta off the coast of Peru and the weather-induced fall in rice and wheat production in several parts of the world during 1972 have led to the current price explosion in basic food items and thereby underlined the urgency of studying and influencing the growth of global agricultural production and consumption trends with regard to both short- and long-term factors.

The Protein Advisory Group views with concern the possible impact of the current food availability and price situation on the nutrition of the vulnerable groups of the developing countries and

more particularly of the landless poor of such nations. It considers that action of the following points is urgently called for:

1. Implementation of the proposal of the Director-General of FAO for achieving "minimum world food security" through a system of coordinated national food reserve policies or through a nonpolitical world food bank.

2. Development of a global approach to the management of world fisheries, including limits on the catch of a number of species and their allocation among countries. The PAG hopes that the countries participating in the forthcoming UN Conference on the Law of the Sea will adopt a constructive approach and help to develop a global fisheries management system which can ensure sustained productivity of marine fisheries, avoidance of pollution and rational distribution of the fish catch. Simultaneously, the PAG urges all developing countries to increase their inland and near-shore fish production through the widespread dissemination of modern aquaculture and mariculture techniques.

3. Research on enhancing animal productivity and improving the yield potential of grain legumes and oil-seeds should receive very high priority. In the United States, which produces 75% of the world's soya bean crop and supplies 90% of all soya beans entering the world market, soya bean yields per acre have increased only about 1% per year since 1950, while the yield of corn has increased by nearly 4% per year during the same period. It is such differential progress in technology which is now placing the food legumes at a disadvantage in cropping systems.

4. Developing countries, generally characterized by low yields per acre but abundant sunshine and favourable conditions for crop growth, offer exciting prospects for expanding food production. Some authorities believe that the current price explosion may be expected, in certain limited situations in a few countries, to lead to income redistribution in favour of poor peasant farmers and thus to nutritional betterment of their diets. However, past experience has shown that this expectation has not always come true, even in these restricted situations. The only solution seems to be that the developed countries should help, at least for some years to come, by providing supplies of inputs such as fertilizers, farm equipment, pumps and similar means of promoting scientific agriculture. These inputs will lead to a reduction in the cost of production, more opportunities for additional employment and an improvement in

income and nutrition among the poorer segments of the populations. Particular attention should be paid to improving the foreign exchange earnings of the less developed countries through the export of both true surplus primary products and finished products manufactured by a well-developed system of agroindustries.

5. The PAG urges agricultural planners in the developed and developing countries to examine the need, ultimate scope and impact of further expansion of the plant-animal-man food chain, both through long-term assessment of the fodder, feed and water requirements of this chain and through a careful study of feasible alternatives including technological developments in the area of substitution of vegetable protein for animal protein. An example of this is the standardization of oil-seed protein-based meat analogs and milk-like beverages.

6. Rising prices spell danger to the nutrition of a large majority of low-income urban populations. The PAG urges national governments to develop systems of food distribution which will ensure the supply of the basic food needs of such vulnerable groups.

7. About 71% of mankind lives in developing countries where only about 44% of the world food supply is produced. The negative impact of the world livestock-feed demand on this population-food ratio calls for careful examination, and policies must be formulated which will not only prevent any adverse effect on the nutritional status of the people of developing nations but will also promote their rural and agricultural living standards.

Bibliography

SECTION 1. FOOD AND NUTRITION SCIENCE

1.1. General publications on human nutrition

Beaton, G. H. & McHenry, E. W. (1966) *Nutrition*, Academic Press, New York and London (3 volumes).

Brock, J. F. (1961) *Recent advances in human nutrition, with special reference to clinical medicine*, Churchill, London.

Davidson, Sir Stanley & Passmore, R. (1969) *Human nutrition and dietetics*, E. & S. Livingstone Ltd., Edinburgh and London (899 pp.).

Gifft, H. H., Washbon, M. B. & Harrison, G. G. (1972) *Nutrition, behavior and change*, Prentice-Hall Inc., Englewood Cliffs (392 pp.).

Jelliffe, D. B. (1962) *Child health in the tropics*, Edward Arnold Ltd., London (144 pp.).

Jelliffe, D. B. (1968) *Child nutrition in the tropics; a handbook for field workers*, Published for US AID Government Print Office, Washington (200 pp.).

Joffe, J. M. (1969). *Prenatal determinants of behaviour*, Pergamon Press, Oxford (366 pp.).

Joliffe, N. (ed.) (1962) *Clinical nutrition* (2nd ed.), Harper & Brothers, New York (1012 pp.).

Nichols, L. (1961) *Tropical nutrition and dietetics*, new edition, Sinclair, H. M. (ed.). Bailliere, Tindall and Co., London (457 pp.).

Waterlow, J. C. & Stephen, J. M. L. (1955) *Human requirements and their fulfilment in practice*; proceedings of a conference in Princeton, 1955, sponsored jointly by FAO, WHO and the Josiah Macy Jr. Foundation, N.Y. (193 pp.).

Wohl, M. G. & Goodheart, R. S. (eds.) (1971) *Modern nutrition in health and disease* (4th ed.), Lea & Febiger, Philadelphia (1239 pp.).

1.2. Protein-calorie malnutrition and nutritional problems of low-income countries

Anonymous (1969) *A practical guide to combating malnutrition in the pre-school child*; report of a working conference, Bogota, Columbia, 1969. Meredith Corp., New York (74 pp.).

Blix, G., Hofvander, Y. & Vahlquist, B. (eds.) (1971) *Famine; a symposium dealing with nutrition and relief operations in times of disaster*. Edited for the Swedish Nutrition Foundation and the Swedish International Development Authority (SIDA) (200 pp.).

Burgers, A. & Dean, R. F. A. (1962) *Malnutrition and food habits*, report of an international and interprofessional conference, Tavistock Publications, London (210 pp.).

György, P. & Burgers, A. (1965) *Protecting the pre-school child*, Tavistock Publications, London (108 pp.).

Hurley, R. H. (1969) *Poverty and mental retardation; a causal relationship*, Vintage Books, New York (301 pp.).

May, J. M. (1965) *The ecology of malnutrition in Middle Africa*, Hafner Publishing Co., New York and London (255 pp.).

McCance, R. A. & Widdowson, E. M. (1968) *Calorie deficiencies and protein deficiencies*; proceedings of a colloquium in Cambridge (USA) 1967. Little, Brown and Co., Boston (386 pp.).

National Academy of Science (1961) *Progress in meeting protein needs of infants and pre-school children*; proceedings of an international conference held in Washington, DC, August 21–24, 1960, under the auspices of the Committee on Protein Malnutrition, Food and Nutrition Board and the Nutrition Study Section, National Institutes of Health; publication no. 843, National Academy of Sciences–National Research Council, Washington.

National Academy of Science (1966) *Pre-school child malnutrition; Primary determinant to human progress*; an international conference, Washington, DC, 1964; publication no. 1282, National Academy of Sciences–National Research Council, Washington (355 pp.).

Robson, J. R. K. (1972) *Malnutrition, its causation and control*, Gordon and Breach, New York, London and Paris (2 volumes).

Scrimshaw, N. S. & Altschul, A. M. (eds.) (1971) *Amino-acid fortification of protein foods*; report of an international conference at MIT, September 16–18, 1969. MIT Press, Cambridge, USA (664 pp.).

Scrimshaw, N. S. & Gordon, J. E. (eds.) (1968) *Malnutrition, learning and behavior*; proceedings of an international conference, March 1–3, 1969. MIT Press, Cambridge, USA.

Vahlquist, Bo (ed.) (1973) *Nutrition; a priority in African development*; proceedings of the 1971 Dag Hammarskjöld Seminar. The Dag Hammarskjöld Foundation, Uppsala, Sweden.

von Muralt, A. (ed.) (1969) *Protein-calorie malnutrition*; a Nestle Foundation Symposium. Springer Verlag, Berlin, Heidelberg and New York (194 pp.).

1.3. Proteins, protein supply and protein foods

Aylward, F. (1971) Food conservation and utilization in different countries, chapter 5, pp. 53–67 in Margen, S. (see below).

Altschul, A. M. (ed.) (1958) *Processed plant protein foodstuffs*, Academic Press, New York (955 pp.).

Altschul, A. M. (1965) *Proteins—their chemistry and politics*, Basic Books, Inc., New York (337 pp.).

Altschul, A. M. (ed.) (1966) *World protein resources*, a symposium sponsored by the Division of Agricultural and Food Chemistry at the 150th Meeting of the American Chemical Society, Atlantic City, J.J., September 13–15, 1965; Advances in Chemistry Series, 57, American Chemical Society, Washington (285 pp.).

Association of Food Technologists (1970) *Protein fortification of foods*, Hindustan Thompson Associates Ltd., New Delhi (125 pp.).

Balint, A. (1970) *Protein growth by plant breeding*, Akademiai Kiado, Budapest.

Belden, G. C. *et al.* (1964) *The protein paradox*, Nimrod Press, Inc., Boston (145 pp.).

Bender, A. E., Kihlberg, R., Löfqvist, B. & Munck, L. (eds.) (1970) *Evaluation of novel protein products*, Pergamon Press, Oxford.

Dean, R. F. A. (1953) *Plant proteins in child feeding*, HMSO, London (163 pp.).

Giddey, C., Hoegl, H., Velay, C., Walker-Leigh, V. & Revillard, F. (1969) *Protein rich foods in India*, a study of the rôle which manufactured protein foods from unconventional and non-conventional sources could play in solving problems of protein malnutrition in India; a report submitted to UNDP. Batelle Institute, Geneva (mimeographed).

Gounelle de Pontanel, H. (1972) *Proteins from hydrocarbons*, Academic Press, London (285 pp.).

Inglett, G. E. (1972) *Symposium: Seed proteins*, Avi, Westport (320 pp.).

Jones, J. G. W. (ed.) (1973) *The biological efficiency of protein production*, Cambridge University Press, Cambridge (385 pp.).

Kracht, U. (1972) *Okonomische Aspekte einer Verbesserung die Eiweissversorgung in Entwicklungsländern durch neuartige eiweissreiche Nahrungsmittel*, Institut für ausländische Landwirtschaft der Technischen Universität Berlin, Berlin (dissertation, 329 pp.).

Lawrie, R. A. (ed.) (1970) *Proteins as human food*, proceedings of the Sixteenth Easter School in Agricultural Science, University of Nottingham, 1969. Butterworths, London, also Avi, Westport (525 pp.).

Mateles, R. I. & Tannenbaum, S. R. (eds.) (1968) *Single-cell protein*, proceedings of a conference in 1967. MIT Press, Cambridge, USA.

Margen, S. (ed.) (1971) *Progress in human nutrition*, Avi, Westport, Conn. (228 pp.).

Milner, M. (ed.) (1969) *Protein-enriched cereal foods for world needs*, The American Association of Cereal Chemists, St. Paul.

Orr, E. & Adair, D. (1967) *The production of protein foods and concentrates from oil-seeds*, Tropical Products Institute, London (104 pp. and 8 appendices).

Pirie, N. W. (1971) *Leaf protein: its agronomy, preparation, quality and use*, IBP Handbook No. 20, Blackwell, Oxford and Edinburgh (192 pp.).

Porter, J. W. G. & Rolls, B. A. (eds.) (1973) *The chemistry, biology and physics of protein evaluation*, proceedings of a meeting in Reading, March 20–24, 1972. Academic Press, New York and London.

1.4. Food science and technology and agro-industries

Appelqvist, L. A. & Ohlson, R. (1972) *Rape-seed; cultivation, composition, processing and utilization*, Elsevier Publishing Co., Amsterdam, London and New York (391 pp.).

Aylward, F. (1969) Requirements for the establishment of a tropical fruit industry, in *Tropical and subtropical fruits*, proceedings of a conference held at the London School of Pharmacy, September 15–19, 1969. Tropical Products Institute, London.

Houston, D. F. (1972) *Rice chemistry and technology*, American Association of Cereal Chemists, St. Paul (517 pp.).

Orr, Elizabeth (1972) *The use of protein-rich foods for the relief of malnutrition in developing countries: an analysis of experience*, Tropical Products Institute, London (71 pp.).

Robinson, W. B., Bourne, M. C. & Steinkrauss, K. H. (1971) *Development of soy-based foods of high nutritive value for use in the Phillipines*, Agency for International Development Contract, Cornell University, Geneva (100 pp.).

Woodroof, J. G. (1966) *Peanuts, production, processing, products*, Avi, Westport (291 pp.).

1.5. Agriculture and food supply

Anonymous. (1969) *Departmental Committee of Inquiry into Allotments*, (Cmnd 4166), HMSO, London (460 pp.).

Brown, Lester R. (1970) *Seeds of change; the green revolution and development in the 1970s*; published for the Overseas Development Council. Praeger, New York, Washington and London.

Critchfield, R. (1971) *It's a revolution all right*, Alicia Patterson Fund, New York.

Harrar, J. G. (1967) *Strategy towards the conquest of hunger*, selected papers of J. George Harrar, President, The Rockefeller Foundation. The Rockefeller Foundation, New York.

Kachroo, P. (ed.) (1970) *Pulse crops of India*, Indian Council of Agricultural Research, New Delhi (334 pp.).

Pirie, N. W. (1969) *Food resources, conventional and novel*, Penguin Books, Baltimore (208 pp.).

The President's Science Advisory Committee (1967) *The World Food Problem*, a report of the President's Science Advisory Committee, The White House, May 1967. Government Printing Office, Washington.

Russell, Sir John (1961) *World population and world food supplies*, George Allen and Unwin, London (513 pp.).

Shaw, R. (1970) *Jobs and agricultural development*, Overseas Development Council, Washington.

Turk, K. L. (ed.) (1971) *Some issues emerging from recent breakthroughs in food production*, Cornell University, Ithaca (496 pp.).

1.6. Studies of food supplies and nutritional status in low-income countries

Amann, V. F., Belshaw, D. G. R. & Stanfield, J. P. (eds.) (1972) *Nutrition and food in an African economy*, Makerere University, Kampala (2 volumes).

American University of Beirut (1971) *Proceedings of symposia on nutrition and health in the Near East* (the sixth of these symposia was held in April 1971 and published in 1971), American University of Beirut, Beirut.

Darby, W. J. & Pharaon, H. M. (1964) *Nutrition survey on infants and pre-school children in Jordan, 1962–63* (175 pp.).

Patwardhan, V. N. & Darby, W. J. (1972) *The state of nutrition in the Arab Middle East*, Vanderbilt University Press, Nashville (308 pp.).

US Agency for International Development (1972) *A study of food habits in Calcutta*, Hindustan Thompson Associates Ltd., Calcutta.

US Department of Health, Education and Welfare (1967) *Republic of Nigeria; Nutrition survey 1965*, US Department of Health, Education and Welfare, Washington (299 pp.).

1.7. Miscellaneous publications

Brockington, F. (1958) *World Health*, Penguin Books Ltd., Harmondsworth (405 pp.).

Hammonds, T. M. & Call, D. L. (1970) *Utilization of protein ingredients in the US food industry*, Cornell University, Ithaca (2 volumes).

Longier, J. D. (1969) *Economical and nutritional diets using scarce resources*, Michigan State University, East Lansing (73 pp.).

Sheffield, J. R. & Diejomaok, V. P. (1972) *Non-formal education in African development*, African-American Institute, New York (258 pp.).

SECTION 2. UNITED NATIONS PUBLICATIONS (GENERAL)

2.1. United Nations Secretariat and United Nations Advisory Committee on the Application of Science and Technology to Development (ACAST)

Where available in print, these documents and publications may be obtained normally in English, French, Spanish and Russian, from the local United Nations sales agent or from United Nations, Sales Section, New York, NY 10017, USA.

Resolutions

The following resolutions pertaining to protein problems have been adopted by the United Nations General Assembly. They are reproduced in mimeographed form only and not available for general distribution.

(1967) Increasing the production and use of edible protein   A/RES/2319(XXII)
(1968) Increase in the production and use of edible protein   A/RES/2416(XXIII)
(1970) Increase in the production and use of edible protein A/RES/2684(XXV)
(1971) Protein resources   A/RES/2848(XXVI)

Reports

The United Nations Secretariat, often with the assistance of expert panels or outside experts, has prepared the following reports, for consideration by the Advisory Committee on the Application of Science and Technology to Development, the Economic and Social Council or the General Assembly.

(1968) Report to the Economic and Social Council by the Advisory Committee on the Application of Science and Technology to Development. *International action to avert the impending protein crisis* (published in book form) E.68,XIII.2.

(1968) Report of the Secretary-General. *The Protein Problem* (mimeographed) E/4592.

(1970) Progress report of the Secretary-General. *Increase in the production and use of edible protein. The protein problem* (mimeographed) E/4829.

(1971) Report of the Panel of Experts on the Protein Problem Confronting Developing Countries. *Strategy statement on action to avert the protein crisis in the developing countries* (printed) E.71.II.A.17.

(1971) Department of Economic and Social Affairs. World plan of action for the application of science and technology to development (286 pp.). E/4926/Rev.1; (E.71.II.A.18).

2.2. Food and Agriculture Organization of the United Nations, (FAO, Rome, Italy)

Where available, printed publications may be obtained in English, French or Spanish from the local FAO sales agent or from FAO, Rome, Italy.

Statistical

(1969) Indicative world plan for agricultural development. Vol. I–III.
(1971) Agricultural commodity projections, 1970–1980.
(1971) Production yearbook; vol. 25 (published annually).
(1971) Trade yearbook; vol. 25 (published annually).
(1971) Yearbook of fishery statistics; (published annually).

Periodicals

Nutrition Newsletter (published quarterly by the Food Policy and Nutrition Division)
Ceres. FAO Review (published bimonthly).

Reports

(1960) Marketing livestock and meat. Marketing Guide No. 3 (209 pp.).
(1965) Nutrition in relation to agricultural production; by I. S. Dema, project sponsored jointly between FAO, WHO, and UNICEF (123 pp.).
(1965) Human Nutrition in tropical Africa; A project jointly sponsored by FAO, WHO and UNICEF (268 pp.).
(1967) Learning better nutrition; by Gene Ritchie; FAO Nutritional Studies No. 20 (264 pp.).
(1967) Food and nutrition procedures in times of disaster. FAO Nutritional Studies No. 21 (96 pp.).
(1968) Nonprotein nitrogen in the nutrition of ruminants (by J. K. Loosti). FAO Agricultural Studies No. 75 (94 pp.).
(1969) Manual on food and nutrition policy; by B. F. Johnston and J. P. Greaves. FAO Nutritional Studies No. 22 (95 pp.).
(1970) Amino-acid contents of foods. FAO Nutritional Studies, No. 24.
(1971) Food balance sheets, 1964–66.
(1971) Technology of the production of cotton-seed flour for use in protein foods. Agricultural Services Bulletin, No. 7 (42 pp.).
(1971) Technology of production of edible flours and protein products from groundnuts. Agricultural Services Bulletin No. 10 (88 pp.).
(1971) Technology of production of edible flours and protein products from soya bean. Agricultural Services Bulletin, No. 11 (151 pp.).
(1971) Cassava processing. Agricultural Services Bulletin, No. 8 (123 pp.).
(1972) Milk and milk products in human nutrition; by S. K. Kon. FAO Nutritional Studies No. 27 (80 pp.).
(1972) Planning and evaluation of applied nutrition programmes; by M. C. Latham; FAO Nutritional Studies, No. 26.
(1961) Food and Nutrition; Report to the Government of Ghana. ETAP No. 1449 by F. Aylward (76 pp.).
(1967) Agriculture and Industrialization FFHC Basic Study No. 17.
(1964) Legumes in Human Nutrition. FAO Nutritional Studies No. 19 by W. R. Aykroyd and J. Doughty.
(1966) Grass Legumes in Africa by W. R. Stanton (183 pp.).

Jointly with WHO

(1966) Report of the Joint FAO/WHO Technical Meeting on methods of planning and evaluation in applied nutrition programmes (77 pp.).

(1962– Joint FAO/WHO Expert Committee on Nutrition. Sixth Report (65 pp.);
1971) 1967 Seventh Report (114 pp.); 1971 Eighth Report (104 pp.).

(1973) Energy and protein requirements, Report of a Joint FAO/WHO ad hoc Expert Committee (118 pp.).

2.3. World Health Organization (Geneva, Switzerland)

Most printed publications are available in English, French, Russian and Spanish.

Periodicals

World Health Bulletin (scientific articles)
WHO Chronicle (review articles)
Health Today (popular articles)

Reports

(1966) The assessment of the nutritional status of the community; by D. B. Jelliffe. Monograph Series No. 53 (271 pp.).

(1968) Infant nutrition in the subtropics and tropics; by D. B. Jelliffe (335 pp.).

(1968) Interactions of nutrition and infections; by N. S. Scrimshaw, C. E. Tayler and J. E. Gordon, Monograph Series No. 57 (329 pp.).

(1969) The health aspects of food and nutrition; a manual for developing countries in the Western Pacific; Regional Office, Manila (380 pp.).

(1972) Report of a PAHO technical group meeting. Guidelines for food fortification in Latin America and the Caribbean; Pan American Health Organization; Scientific publication No. 240 (48 pp.).

(1972) Human development and public health; report of a WHO scientific group; WHO Technical Report Series No. 485.

2.4. United Nations Childrens' Fund (UNICEF)

United Nations, New York, USA.

Periodicals

Assignment children (an occasional publication)
(A number of FAO, WHO and PAG publications have been sponsored by UNICEF.)

2.5. United Nations' Educational, Scientific and Cultural Organization (Unesco)

Place de Fontenoy, Paris 7e, France.

(1969) *Bi-lateral institutional links in science and technology.* Science policy studies and documents No. 13 (98 pp.).

(1972) *Food and Nutrition Education and Training* with particular reference to the general education system in developing countries, by F. Aylward (54 pp.).

2.6. United Nations' Industrial Development Organization (UNIDO) (Vienna)

Some technical publications on different aspects of food processing such as:
(1973) *Information sources on the vegetable oil processing industry* (90 pp.).
(1970) *Integrated food processing in Yugoslavia* (120 pp.).

2.7. Other United Nations organizations

(1970) Improving plant protein by nuclear techniques. Proceedings of a symposium, Vienna, June 1970, jointly organized by IAEA and FAO, IAEA, Vienna (458 pp.).

(1968) New approaches to breeding for improved plant protein. Proceedings of a panel June, 1968, organized by the joint FAO/IAEA Division. IAEA, Vienna (193 pp.).

(1965) The role of multilateral food aid programs. World Food Programme; Studies No. 5. WFP, Rome.

(1963) The needs of children. Reports prepared by UNICEF, WHO, FAO, Unesco, the UN Bureau of Social Affairs and ILD; General editor, G. Sicault, UNICEF, New York (175 pp.).

SECTION 3. PROTEIN ADVISORY GROUP OF THE UNITED NATIONS SYSTEM (PAG)

When available, these publications listed below may be obtained (normally in English) from the PAG Secretariat, United Nations, New York 10017, USA.

Periodical

3.1.
PAG Bulletin. (Technical information on world protein nutrition of interest to individuals, academic institutions and industrial organizations interested in helping solve protein problems and aims at promoting an exchange of information in this field. It is sent without charge to persons, organizations, and companies with an active interest in proteins.) Published quarterly in English, French and Spanish.

3.2. PAG statements and recommendations

The PAG has from time to time issued statements to serve as the basis for policy orientation and action. (Some have been published in the above mentioned *PAG Bulletin.*)

No.	Title	Date
2	PAG Recommendation of aflatoxin	1969
3	PAG Statement on the nature and magnitude of the protein problem	1971
4	PAG Statement on single cell protein	1970
5	PAG Statement on the marketing and distribution of protein-rich foods	1971
6	PAG Statement on milk substitutes	1970

7	PAG Recommendation on prevention of food losses and protein-calorie malnutrition	1969
8	PAG Statement on plant improvement by genetic means	1970
9	PAG Recommendation on amino-acid fortification of foods	1970
10	PAG Statement on a systems approach to the formulation and evaluation of nutrition intervention programmes	1970
11	PAG Statement on leaf protein concentrate	1970
12	PAG Statement on the world protein problem: research and development needs	1971
13a	Review of the specific proposals contained in ACAST reports "International Action to Avert the Impending Protein Crisis" United Nations, 1968	1971
14	PAG Statement on marketing of conventional foods	1971
15	PAG Statement on popular participation and community involvement in nutrition improvement programmes	1971
16	PAG Statement on the potential of fish protein concentrate for developing countries	1971
17	PAG Statement on low lactase activity and milk intake	1972
18	PAG Statement on relationship of pre- and post-natal malnutrition in children to mental development, learning and behaviour	1972
19	PAG Statement on maintenance and improvement of nutritional quality of protein foods	1972
20	PAG Statement on the "Protein problem"	1973
21	PAG Statement on specifications for solvents	1972
22	PAG Statement on upgrading human nutrition through the improvement of food legumes (38 pp.)	1973
23	PAG Recommendations for the promotion of processed protein foods for vulnerable groups	1972
24	The Green Revolution and protein supplies	1973
25	The global maldistribution of protein: a growing trend	1973
26	Food and nutrition considerations in national economic planning	1973
27	Mass communications in nutrition education	1974

3.3. PAG guidelines

The PAG has adopted guidelines on technical aspects of protein food production and composition and protein nutrition.

No.	Title	Date
2	PAG Guideline for preparing food-quality groundnut flour	1970
4	PAG Guideline for preparation of edible cotton-seed protein concentrate	1970
5	PAG Guideline for edible, heat-processed soy grits and flour	1969
6	PAG Guideline for preclinical testing of novel sources of protein	1970
7	PAG Guideline for human testing of supplementary food mixtures	1970
8	PAG Guideline on protein-rich mixtures for use as weaning foods	1972
9	PAG Guideline on fish protein concentrate	1971
10	PAG Guideline on marketing of protein-rich foods in developing countries (87 pp.)	1971

11 PAG Guideline for the sanitary production and use of dry protein
foods   1972
12 PAG Guideline on the production of single cell protein for human
consumption   1972
13 PAG Guideline for the preparation of milk substitutes of vegetable
origin and toned milk containing vegetable protein   1972
14 PAG Guideline on the preparation of defatted edible sesame flour   1972

3.4. PAG Reports

The PAG has prepared some reports pertaining to protein nutrition.

Title   *Date*

Feeding the pre-school child; report of a PAG ad hoc working group
(62 pp.).   1971
Manual on feeding infants and young children; Cameron & Y. Hofvander
(239 pp.).   1973
The use of protein-rich foods for the relief of malnutrition in developing
countries: an analysis of experience; by Elisabeth Orr; produced as a
report for the PAG and published on its behalf by the Tropical
Products Institute, London (71 pp.).   1972
Lives in peril; protein and the child (published by FAO on behalf of PAG in
English, French and Spanish, 52 pp.).   1970
Nutritional improvement of food legumes by breeding; M. Minner (ed.).   1973

3.5. PAG review papers

As background documents for meetings of the PAG, its Secretariat has obtained a
very large number of papers reviewing aspects of protein food production,
protein nutrition and related matters. A few are quoted below.

Nutrition

Bengoa, J. M. (1969) Recent trends on prevalence of PCM (14 pp.)   PAG Doc.
1.2.1/1
PAG (1969) Nutrition *in utero* and in the first months of life (22 pp.)   PAG Doc.
1.14/2
Mata (1970) Field studies on nutrition and infection   PAG Doc. 1.14/6
Monckeberg (1970) Nutrient requirements of infants and young children   PAG
Doc. 1.14/11
Flores (1970) Pre-school child food consumption surveys   PAG Doc. 1.14/10
Rueda-Williamson (1971) Use of childhood mortality studies in planning and
developing public health programmes   PAG Doc. 1.14/24
Satge (1971) Medical, socio-economic and public health indicators of the risk of
malnutrition in mothers and children   PAG Doc. 1.14/22

Breast Feeding

Dahlquist & Lindquist (1970) Lactose intolerance and Protein malnutrition   PAG
Doc. 1.14/14

Jelliffe & Jelliffe (1970) A world survey of breast feeding   PAG Doc. 1.14/8

Niehoff & Meister (1970) The cultural characteristics of breast feeding: a survey   PAG Doc. 1.14/12

Infant Feeding and Weaning Foods

Jelliffe & Jelliffe (1971) The at-risk concept and young child nutrition programmes   PAG Doc. 1.14/18

Tagle (1972) The use of chickpea in infant feeding   PAG Doc. 1.14/28

Luyken (1972) Human feeding on green leafy vegetables and legumes   PAG Doc. 1.14/29

Srikantia (1972) Use of legumes and green leafy vegetables in feeding infants and young children   PAG Doc. 1.14/30

Rajalakshmi (1972) Formulation and evaluation of low-cost balanced means using cereals, legumes and leafy vegetables   PAG Doc. 1.14/31

Devadas (1972) Use of legumes and green leafy vegetables for infants and young child feeding   PAG Doc. 1.14/32

FAO/WHO (1970) The work of the codex alimentarius commission on standards and legislation on infants foods   PAG Doc. 1.14/7

Muller (1972) Legislative and regulatory aspects in feeding the pre-school child   PAG Doc. 1.14/33

Protein-rich Foods

Shaw, R. L. (1967) Legislation concerning protein-rich foods for children (12 pp.)   PAG Doc. 18/1

Patankar, V. N. (1969) Protein foods market development programme in India (12 pp.)   PAG Doc. 2.22/17

Ballarin, O. (1969) Potentials of milk substitutes for developing countries (15 pp.)   PAG Doc. 2.11/13

PAG (1972) Current status of protein-rich weaning foods in different countries (9 pp.)   PAG Doc. 2.19/25

Testing Protein-rich Foods

Guzman, Scrimshaw, DeMayer *et al.* (1970) Suggestions for the design and execution of field studies to evaluate measures for improving protein nutritional status (11 pp.)   PAG Doc. 2.36/2

Gordon, J. E. (1971) Field trial of a projected nutrition intervention (31 pp.)   PAG Doc. 2.36/3

Dairy Products

McGillivray, W. A. & L. P. J. Chapman (1969) New Zealand. Wholemilk biscuit (11 pp.)   PAG Doc. 2.7/3

Buchanan, R. A. (1969) The Australian milk biscuit (5 pp.)   PAG Doc. 2.7/4

Gabr (1971) Scientific rationale for the use of acidified and fermented milks in feeding infants and young children   PAG Doc. 1.14/16

Ballarin (1971) The scientific rationale for the use of acidified and fermented milk in feeding infants and young children   PAG Doc. 1.14/19

Tatochenko (1971) Scientific rationale for the use of fermented milk in infant feeding   PAG Doc. 1.14/20

Lactose Intolerance

Reddy (1971) Studies on milk intolerance   PAG Doc. 1.27/2

Luyken (1971) Studies on milk intolerance: A review of literature for Latin America   PAG Doc. 1.27/3

PAG (1971) Milk Intolerance: Practical implications   PAG Doc. 1.27/4

Latham & Macquarrie (1971) The pathogenesis of milk intolerance with special reference to lactose intolerance   PAG Doc. 1.27/5

Vahlquist, B. (1971) Prevalence of milk intolerance—Europe and North America   PAG Doc. 1.27/6

Graham (1971) Criteria and usefulness of tests for diagnosis of milk intolerance   PAG Doc. 1.27/7

Ransome-Kuti (1971) Nutritional implications of the use of milk and milk products in the treatment of PCM and in milk feeding programmes   PAG Doc. 1.27/8

Ransome-Kuti (1971) Prevalence and significance of milk intolerance in Africa and Middle East   PAG Doc. 1.27/19

Fishery Products

Monckeberg, F., Donoso, G., Chichester, C. O., Ballester, D. and Yáñes, E. (1970) Practical possibilities for using FPC in the Chilian diet (19 pp.)   PAG Doc. 2.8/29

Burgess, G. H. O. (1971) The alternative uses of fish (47 pp.)   PAG Doc. 2.28/33

Oil-seeds, Nuts and Legumes

Texas Engineering Experiment Station (1965) A report on investigation of meats preparation and screw pressing for production of cotton-seed cake suitable for human food (35 pp.)   PAG Doc. 1/16

Fisher, R. W. (1967) A review of the advantages and disadvantages of the production and utilization of soy beans for human feeding in areas where it is not yet produced or traditionally consumed (15 pp.)   PAG Doc. 1/22

Deschamps, I., Calderon, R. & Gonzales, A. (1966) Protein concentrates from sesame (9 pp.)   PAG Doc. 13/7 R.5/ADD

Nutrition Unit, WHO (1967) Favism and broad beans (vicia faba) (2 pp.)   PAG Doc. 13/7

Kapsiotis, G. D. (1967) Developments on sunflower seed protein concentrates (5 pp.)   PAG Doc. 12/4

Loo, C. C. A collection of Far-Eastern recipies using coconut (30 pp.)   PAG Doc. 9/7 App. 1

Loo, C. C. (1968) A survey of home consumption of fresh coconuts in some Far-Eastern countries (15 pp.)   PAG Doc. 9/7

Liakey, C. L. A. & Rubaihayo, R. (1969) Soy bean production potential and genotype evaluation near the equator in East Africa (10 pp.)   PAG Doc. 2.29/7

Hartwig, E. E. (1969) Improved protein production by soy beans (4 pp.)   PAG Doc. 2.29/3

Kurien, P. P. & Parpia, H. A. B. (1969) Improved method for milling of pulses for higher outturn (5 pp.)   PAG Doc. 2.29/5

Urs, M. K. & Kausalya, K. R. (1971) STudies on preparation of edible grade meal from mustard seeds (8 pp.)   PAG Doc. 2.35/5

Ballaster, D., Yanez, E., Owen, D. F., Chister, C. O. & Monckeberg, F. (1971) Detoxification of rape-seed meal (3 pp.)   PAG Doc. 2.35/4

Gopaldas, Ramakrishman & Grewal (1972) Consumption of legumes and pulses by infants and young children in rural Madhya Pradish, India   PAG Doc. 1.14/35

Ohlson, R. (1973) Rape-seed protein concentrate for human consumption (4 pp.)   PAG Doc. 2.38/5

Mycotoxins

Shank, R. C. & Wogan, G. N. (1971) Mycotoxin contamination of food and food-stuffs in Southeast Asia (9 pp.)   PAG Doc. 2.17/35

Goldblatt, L. A. & Dollear, F. G. (1969) Progress on elimination of aflatoxins from agricultural products (23 pp.)   PAG Doc. 2.17/27

Peers, F. G. & Linsell, C. A. (1969) Field projects on the possible association of liver cancer and aflatoxin (5 pp.)   PAG Doc. 2.17/26

Grains

Lonnquist, J. H. High lysine maize (5 pp.)   PAG Doc. 2.31/3

Harpstead, D. D. (1969) Maize with improved protein (5 pp.)   PAG Doc. 2.31/2

Larter, E. N. (1969) Triticale—a potentially high protein food (9 pp.)   PAG Doc. 2.34/1

IRRI (1969) Improvement of the protein content of rice (13 pp.)   PAG Doc. 2.33/1

Pomeranz, Y. (1973) Proteins in barley, oats and buckwheat (17 pp.)   PAG Doc. 2/2

Milk Substitutes

FAO (1969) Note on legislation of various countries concerning the use and designation of various milk substitutes (In French, 6 pp.)   PAG Doc. 2.11/9

Halens, H. L. & Milner, M. (1969) Imitation milk (8 pp.)   PAG Doc. 2.11/10

De, S. S. (1969) Potentials of milk substitutes in developing countries   PAG Doc. 2.11/11

Loo, C. C. (1969) Potential of milk substitutes in some Far-Eastern countries (12 pp.)   PAG Doc. 2.11/8

Textured Vegetable Proteins (TVP)

Odell, A. D. (1971) Meat analogs—potential in developing countries (9 pp.)   PAG Doc. 2.44/1

Horan, F. E. (1971) Potential for textured vegetable protein (TVP) in Thailand (24 pp.)   PAG Doc. 2.44/2

Leaf Protein (LPC)

Bickoff, E. M. & Kohler, G. O. (1972) Commercial production of leaf protein for animal and human use (3 pp.)   PAG Doc. 2.30/3

Single Cell Proteins

Edozien, J. C. (1969) Yeast for human feeding—new data on safety (9 pp.)   PAG Doc. 2.23/1

Mauron, J. & Wuhrmann, J. J. (1971) Protecel, a new type of SCP product for food use (15 pp.)   PAG Doc. 2.23/7

Spicer, A. (1971) Protein production by micro-fungi (11 pp.)   PAG Doc. 2.23/4

Food Science and Technology

Parpia, H. A. B. (1969) Food grain losses and the nutritional gap in developing countries (12 pp.)   PAG Doc. 1.15/1

Bender, A. E. (1970) Processing damage to protein foods (18 pp.)   PAG Doc. 1.15/2

Tsen, C. C. & Hoover, W. J. (1971) Emulsifiers for the improvement of protein fortified bread (22 pp.)   PAG Doc. 2.42/1

Hagenmeier, R. P., Quinitio and Mattil, K. F. (1972) Coconut protein technology (6 pp.)   PAG Doc. 2.9/9

Research, Information and Documentation

Li, M.-Y. (1970) The need for documentation services in the field of protein foods development (36 pp.)   PAG Doc. 1.4.4/1

Parpia, H. A. B. (1971) Food technology research and training requirements with particular reference to South and South-east Asia (42 pp.)   PAG Doc. 1.17/3

Chichester, C. O. (1972) Food and nutrition research and training institutes (57 pp.)   PAG Doc. 1.33/2

Policy

Mellander, O. & Vahlquist, B. (1970) The need for special regional nutrition teams for survey, training and relief purposes   PAG Doc. 1.14/4

Simon, S. R., Cesario, F. Kinne, I. L. & Yates, D. M. (1970) A systems approach to the world protein problem (38 pp.)   PAG Doc. 1.13/2

Levinson, F. J. & Call, D. L. (1970) Nutrition intervention in low-income countries: Its economic rôle and alternative strategies; a model for nutrition planning (38 pp.)   PAG Doc. 1.13/1

Devanny III (1971) Generation of minimum cost infant foods (21 pp.)   PAG Doc. 2.8/31

Gongora y Lopez, J. (1972) Some suggestions regarding intervention action programs for the feeding of vulnerable groups (pregnant and lactating women, weaning infants and pre-school children) (7 pp.)   PAG Doc. 1.17/8

Wishik, S. M. (1972) Nutrition, family planning and fertility (12 pp.)   PAG Doc. 1.29/1

Evaluation

Forman, M. (1971) Guidelines for evaluation of supplementary feeding programs for pre-school children   PAG Doc. 1/14/25

Beghin, I. D. & Viteri, F. (1971) Nutritional rehabilitation centres: an evaluation of their performance (71 pp.)   PAG Doc. 1.23/1

Schmaedick, G. L. (1972) Evaluation of the US Food for Peace program (5 pp.)   PAG Doc. 1.17/9

Index

Printed in Great Britain by
J. W. Arrowsmith Ltd., Bristol BS3 2NT.